Evaluating Costs and Outcomes

Demonstrating the Value of Rehabilitation Services

Diane E. Watson, MBA, OTR

The American Occupational Therapy Association, Inc.
4720 Montgomery Lane
PO Box 31220
Bethesda, Maryland 20824-1220

Disclaimers
This publication is designed to provide accurate and authoritative information in regard to the subject matter covered. It is sold or distributed with the understanding that the publisher is not engaged in rendering legal, accounting, or other professional service. If legal advice or other expert assistance is required, the services of a competent professional person should be sought.
—From the Declaration of Principles jointly adopted by the American Bar Association and a Committee of Publishers and Associations.

It is the objective of The American Occupational Therapy Association to be a forum for free expression and interchange of ideas. The opinions expressed by the contributors to this work are their own and not necessarily those of either the editors or The American Occupational Therapy Association.

ISBN 1-56900-138-3

*To my son Austin Jeffery and
in loving memory of
Jeffery Eugene*

Contents

Foreword

Mary Foto, OT, FAOTA, CCM

As occupational therapy practitioners, we stand on the threshold of both significant challenges to our autonomy and unprecedented opportunities to expand our practice roles. To successfully meet our challenges and seize opportunities, we must first be capable of functioning within the dynamics of today's health care environment; an environment in which drastic changes have occurred in the funding and delivery of health care. These changes are driven by aggressive competition among providers, demanding health care users and payers, and the ever-increasing demand for managed care. To succeed in this environment, we must continue to evolve the value of our professional status as well as to be valued for our economic usefulness. To be valued, we must capably respond to the central question posed by those who consume our services, those who employ us to provide them, and those who pay for them: "What is the value of what we produce?"

Thus, to thrive today and grow into tomorrow, we must be of value to *all* of our customers. Regardless of the patient population that we serve, regardless of whether we work in an acute care setting, rehabilitation center, clinic, community-based program, private practice, or medical treatment unit in a public school, occupational therapy practitioners will be called upon to provide services that are viewed as valuable to all stakeholders. In the past, *quality* of care was the watchword. Today, the goal of service provision is also *value*. Quality of care is assumed, and value is expected. In the past, we were challenged to answer the question, "Does what we do produce results?" The question being asked of us today is quite different. Today we are asked, "Do the results that we produce make a difference—do our outcomes justify our services?" That is, are our services of value?

Evaluating Costs and Outcomes: Demonstrating the Value of Rehabilitation Services is a phenomenal resource that will help you to successfully come to grips with this question and to objectively answer "yes." This book will provide you with the conceptual framework within which to understand health care's concept of value, and it will provide you with the practical tools required to objectively define, measure, and effectively communicate the value of your services.

Preface

Early in my career as an occupational therapist I became interested in how health service resources might be equitably distributed among persons in need of care. I was particularly concerned about our apparent inability to determine which persons with chronic needs should continue or not continue to receive care, justify what frequency or intensity of rehabilitation services was optimal, and determine which type of rehabilitation care was most cost-effective. These dilemmas ultimately require that we evaluate our services to identify cost-effective interventions and then allocate our limited health care resources to persons who most benefit from this type of care. It is through the pursuit of knowledge regarding the costs and outcomes of various rehabilitation services that we will eventually be able to select the right intervention for the right person and provide it in the right intensity, at the right time, and in the right setting. I believe that these issues will characterize the newest paradigm in health services research and delivery.

The identification of cost-effective services requires that purchasers, service deliverers, and practitioners determine and compare the costs and outcomes of different health care programs, interventions, and services. Providing evidence regarding the effectiveness of therapeutic intervention is not adequate unless this information is coupled with an understanding of the resources required to render a service and achieve a specified outcome. The economic evaluation methods described in this book provide a systematic approach by which the cost and clinical effectiveness of different interventions can be described and compared to help decision makers in determining the relative value of these services.

While economic evaluations have been conducted by economists in different industrial sectors for some time, their application to health services is relatively new. Therefore, the medical literature in this area often contains conflicting terminology and methodological recommendations. However, throughout this text I have tried to conform to the nomenclature recommended by experts who have recently attempted to standardize the different types of economic evaluation. In addition, this text has been designed to develop a basic understanding among rehabilitation practitioners regarding the components of an economic evaluation. Readers who are interested in more complex methodological issues should consult the references listed in Appendix B.

To date, the number of economic evaluations that have been conducted to assess the value of rehabilitation services is small in comparison to the number of effectiveness studies. In addition, the assessments that have been done are primarily in the domains of fieldwork education and administration rather than clinical services (Watson & Mathews, 1998). Interestingly, information regarding the cost and outcomes of fieldwork and various administrative mechanisms has been sought by people within the profession. I believe that economic evaluations must be conducted in the clinical areas within which occupational therapists practice if we are to demonstrate the contribution of rehabilitation services to improve the health of the population. Priority should be given to conducting assessments with the clients and within the service settings and domains of functional performance that are the focus of the majority of practitioners. This information is now being sought by people outside of the profession. Without the knowledge gained from economic evaluations, decisions regarding the allocation of financial resources will not be based on evidence and rehabilitation practitioners will not be able to lead or inform discussions regarding the relative value of established or innovative programs and services.

Evaluating the cost-effectiveness of rehabilitation services requires that we take two risks: (a) we must conduct assessments to determine whether specific interventions are effective at attaining desirable outcomes, and (b) we must evaluate these effective interventions to ensure that they offer the most efficient means of attaining these outcomes. Although many practitioners and researchers have pursued the first undertaking, I hope that this text will stimulate interest in those who wish to take the second plunge.

Reference

Watson, D. E., & Mathews, M. (1998). Economic evaluation of occupational therapy: Where are we at? *Canadian Journal of Occupational Therapy, 65,* 160–167.

Acknowledgments

The conceptual foundations for this book must be credited to the educators at the Faculty of Business Administration at the University of Western Ontario and the Department of Health Administration at the University of Toronto in Canada, who taught me about financial accounting and effectiveness research and influenced my thoughts about equity in resource allocation. A special thank you to the professors in the Evaluation and Outcomes section of the doctoral program at the University of Toronto.

This project received a publication grant from the Canadian Occupational Therapy Foundation in 1998. The support offered by this organization provided me with early assurances that the rehabilitation community would value the information contained in this book.

Various versions of this manuscript have been reviewed by my friend and colleague Maria Mathews, MHSA, BA, BSc. Maria provided me with countless comments and suggestions; and she must be credited as a contributory author for the chapters titled "Designing and Managing an Evaluation," "Cost-Utility and Cost-Benefit Analyses," and "Enhancing Methodological Rigor." I am also grateful to other persons at the American Occupational Therapy Association (AOTA) and the occupational therapy community who provided me with feedback during the planning stages of this project as well as editorial assistance with early drafts. I would also like to recognize the valuable feedback provided by Deborah Lieberman, MHSA, OTR/L, FAOTA, who is a Practice Associate at AOTA.

I am particularly thankful to my husband Gregg Landry, BS, OTR, OT Reg., who always supports my "small" projects in "big" ways; and to Austin, my little baby, who watches with wide eyes and big smiles as I type and type.

Section I

Introduction to Evaluation

1
Demonstrating the Value of Clinical Services

The new health care environment and our professional ethics demand that we be able to predict, on average or within a certain range, the outcome of treatment before it begins; achieve that outcome on or before the predicted date; provide the highest possible, most sustainable level of functional improvement at the lowest cost; and offer satisfaction to our customers. This approach represents a paradigm shift from doing everything and anything for our individual client, regardless of outcome or cost, to focusing on areas of specific expertise and proven value. (Foto, 1998, p. 7)

Over the last number of decades, concerns over the cost and outcome of health services and programs have grown. Consumers continue to demand high-quality clinical care, but have become increasingly concerned about the size and growth in the amount of money they spend on health care. Payers have become more sophisticated buyers, as there is substantial evidence that there is variability in the quality, cost, and appropriateness of services rendered by different service deliverers. Public policymakers have targeted health care as a priority for reform, as national expenditures on medical services are increasing without measurable improvement in overall health and well-being. Health service administrators and practitioners have focused more effort on improving and demonstrating the effectiveness and efficiency of their services in response to these pressures.

We are moving away from an era of unlimited health services that focused on doing everything and anything for an individual client irrespective of cost and outcome to a new era that focuses on the equitable and appropriate allocation of scarce and costly resources (Foto, 1998). The current challenge is to offer services to persons who have the potential to achieve worthwhile outcomes, while avoiding the provision of "futile services that raise false hopes and waste scarce resources" (Joe, 1998, p. 12). The primary goal of national, state, and local service delivery initiatives is to offer more cost-effective services by providing the right service to the right person, at the right time, and in the right setting.

There is a large body of literature dating back to the 1970s that suggests that there is substantial variability in the quality, cost, and appropriateness of services rendered by different health care delivery systems. (Wennberg & Gittelsohn, 1973). It would appear that the type and volume of health services provided to persons is dependent on where they live in the country (Cohen & Tumlinson, 1997; Steinberg, 1993). For example, Lee, Huber, and Stason (1996) conducted a study of Medicare recipients and found evidence of wide geographic disparity in the use of poststroke rehabilitation, the settings in which these services are rendered, and the cost per stroke survivor after regions of the country were standardized such that they represented patients with the same age, gender, and type of stroke. This type of geographic variability in poststroke rehabilitation suggests that "natural experiments" are occurring in the community, as health care service providers offer different interventions that result in various costs and outcomes. Evaluations could be done to identify the most optimal type and volume of services to offer to people who are recovering from cerebral vascular accidents. The most optimal service is the intervention that offers the most value.

In addition, there is substantial evidence that health care service providers vary in the fees they charge for a specific service as well as the outcomes they achieve (Cohen & Tumlinson, 1997; Cowper et al., 1997; Lee et al., 1996; Selby et al., 1996; Weiner, Starfield, Powe, Stuart, & Steinwachs, 1996). This variability in services, charges, and outcomes can not be explained by differences in patients insurance coverage, the availability of delivery of health care services, the prevalence or incidence of disease, or the socioeconomic and health status of service recipients (Stockwell & Vayda, 1979; Volinn et al., 1992; Wennberg & Gittlesohn, 1973). If health care service providers vary in the fees they charge and the outcomes they achieve, evaluations could be done to identify the services that achieve the greatest effect on the health of a defined clientele at the lowest cost.

The quality and cost of health care are often posed as competing objectives. In other words, people tend to expect that high-quality services are more costly than care that is rated lower quality. However, research suggests that there is not a clear association between these dimensions of health service (Haas-Wilson, 1994; Starfield et al., 1994). Therefore, evaluations could be conducted to identify high-quality services that are available at a low cost to meet the health needs of a defined clientele.

It would appear that a sizable portion of the health services that are rendered by service providers are inappropriate (Leape, 1989; Park et al., 1986). In other words, the expected health benefit derived by patients who received these interventions does not appear to exceed the expected negative consequences by a sufficiently wide enough margin that the service is worth providing (Lavis & Anderson, 1996; Sharpe & Faden, 1996). Conversely, services that are expected to do more good than harm are also not provided (Horton, Romans, & Cruess, 1992). If health care delivery systems render services that are considered inappropriate and do not provide services that are deemed appropriate, evaluations could be conducted to identify which service providers and interventions adequately meet the health needs of a defined clientele.

All of this evidence suggests that there is substantial room for improving the effectiveness and efficiency of health service programs. The challenge is to assess the cost and outcome of different interventions and thereby provide decision makers with information regarding the relative value of each service. *Value* refers to "a fair return or equivalent in goods, services, or money for something exchanged," or the "relative worth, utility, or importance of something" (*Merriam-Webster's Collegiate Dictionary*, 1984, p. 1303). Therefore, within the health care context, the term *value* refers to the relative worth, utility, or importance of a service in meeting the health needs of a defined clientele.

In response to this challenge, there has been increased attention during the 1990s toward the development of methods to evaluate and demonstrate the relative value of various clinical services. For example, in 1993 the Public Health Service in the United States convened a Panel on Cost-Effectiveness in Health and Medicine to develop a framework to standardize the analytical methods used to evaluate different health conditions and interventions that included preventative, therapeutic, rehabilitative, and public health (White House Domestic Policy Council, 1993). The Agency for Health Care Policy and Research, Centers for Disease Control, Food and Drug Administration, and National Institutes of Health have also trained staff to conduct cost-effectiveness analyses to evaluate services and develop practice guidelines (Neumann, Zinner, & Paltiel, 1996; Russell, Gold, Siegel, Daniels, & Weinstein, 1996).

The current marketplace requires that all health care service providers have an understanding of the cost and outcomes of the services they render and appraise evidence in health care literature regarding the value of other interventions. Although persons in the health industry have spent time and effort assessing and demonstrating the effectiveness of different interventions and models of care, relatively few publications in the rehabilitation literature demonstrate the cost associated with different outcomes (Watson & Mathews, 1998). Balas et al. (1998) conducted a systematic review of the literature and found that although authors make statements regarding the cost implications of health interventions, a large majority do not publish actual numbers.

The purpose of this book is to provide current and future practitioners, administrators, and researchers with a basic understanding of how to identify and estimate the most relevant cost and outcomes of an intervention and appraise evidence regarding the relative value of a health service. The bulk of this book focuses on the use and appraisal of economic evaluations. These evaluations offer investigators a systematic method by which to describe and compare the cost and outcomes of health interventions to determine the relative worth or value of different services (Drummond, O'Brien, Stoddart, & Torrance, 1997). These assessments help health care service providers demonstrate the value of their programs and help purchasers and consumers to appreciate and compare the relative value of different services.

The value of a clinical service is dependent on the perspective of the person who is making this determination. For example, it is likely that patients value services that are responsive to their needs, timely, user-friendly, convenient, and satisfying. Payers most likely value services that demonstrate good cost-benefit ratios, prevent complications, return patients to the highest possible level of productivity, and satisfy consumers. Health care providers probably value services that generate positive outcomes at low cost, maintain existing and generate new managed care contracts, and satisfy consumers. In summary, these stakeholders all value services that are cost-effective and satisfy consumers (Foto, 1998).

Chapter 2 provides an introduction to the different types of clinical, program, and economic evaluations used in health care. Chapter 3 offers suggestions and strategies on how to design and manage an economic evaluation. Chapters 4 and 5 describe the methods that can be used to demonstrate the value of various health interventions. Specific approaches to identifying and measuring the outcomes and costs of care are provided in the subsequent two chapters. The final chapter in Section II highlights some of the complex issues inherent in conducting economic evaluations. Investigators who have completed an evaluation and will be demonstrating the value of clinical services should consult chapters 9 and 10 in Section III.

Each chapter begins with a list of objectives to assist readers in structuring and monitoring the learning process. Evaluations that have been published in the literature are used as examples throughout the book to illustrate concepts and methodological techniques. These articles can be used as role models for persons who will be conducting evaluations of various rehabilitation services. Practice exercises are located at the end of each chapter to provide readers with the opportunity to actively participate in conducting an evaluation. A list of learning resources is provided in most of the chapters. Appendix A offers a list of popular outcomes measurement instruments. Appendixes B and C provide bibliographic references of methodological issues and economic evaluations that may be of interest to the rehabilitation community. Answers to the practice exercises are provided in Appendix D.

Times are changing. We are moving away from an era where service delivery systems could offer an unlimited array of health services to a climate that focuses on the equitable allocation of cost-effective services. The identification of cost-effective services requires that all service providers have an understanding of the cost and outcomes of the services they render and appraise evidence in the literature regarding the value of other interventions. Our clients expect that our interventions are effective and that our practice is based on evidence (Law & Baum, 1998). The purpose of this book is to provide information to help readers develop a basic understanding of how to evaluate and demonstrate the value of rehabilitation services. Without the knowledge gained from these assessments, resource allocation decisions will not be based on evidence, and rehabilitation practitioners will not be able to lead or inform discussions regarding the value of established or innovative programs and services. ❖

References

Balas, E. A., Kretschmer, R. A. C., Gnann, W., West, D. A., Boren, S. A., Center, R. M., Nerlich, M., Gupta, M., West, T. D., Soderstrom, N. S. (1998). Interpreting cost analyses of clinical interventions. *Journal of the American Medical Association, 279,* 54–57.

Cohen, M. A., & Tumlinson, A. (1997). Understanding the state variation in Medicare home health care: The impact of Medicaid program characteristics, state policy, and provider attributes. *Medical Care, 35,* 618–633.

Cowper, P. A., DeLong, E. R., Peterson, E. D., Lipscomb, J., Muhlbaier, L. H., Jollis, J. G., Pryor, D. B., & Mark, D. B. (1997). Geographic variation in resource use for coronary artery bypass surgery. *Medical Care, 35,* 320–333.

Drummond, M. F., O'Brien, B. J., Stoddart, G. L., & Torrance, G. (1997). *Methods for the economic evaluation of health care programmes* (2nd ed.). Oxford, UK: Oxford University Press.

Foto, M. (1998). From my office. *OT Week for Today's Student, Spring,* 7.

Haas-Wilson, D. (1994). The relationships between the dimensions of health care quality and price: The case of eye care. *Medical Care, 32,* 175–182.

Horton, J., Romans, M., & Cruess, D. (1992). Mammography attitudes and usage study, 1992. *Women's Health Issues 2,* 190–186.

Joe, B. (1998). Strong leadership in changing times. *OT Week, 12*(13), 12–13.

Lavis, J. N., & Anderson, G. M. (1996). Appropriateness in health care delivery: Definitions, measurement and policy implications. *Canadian Medical Association Journal, 154,* 321–328.

Law, M., & Baum, C. (1998). Evidence-based occupational therapy. *Canadian Journal of Occupational Therapy, 65,* 131–135.

Leape, L. L. (1989). Unnecessary surgery. *Health Services Research, 24,* 351–407.

Lee, A. J., Huber, J., & Stason, W. B. (1996). Poststroke rehabilitation in older Americans: The Medicare experience. *Medical Care, 34*, 811–825.

Merriam-Webster's Ninth New Collegiate Dictionary. (1984). Springfield, MA: Merriam-Webster.

Neumann, P. J., Zinner, D. E., & Paltiel, A. D. (1996). The FDA and regulation of cost-effective claims. Health Affairs (*Millwood*), *15*(3), 54–71.

Park, R. E., Fink, A., Brook, R. H., Chassin, M.R. et al., (1986). Physician ratings of appropriate indications for six medical and surgical procedures. *American Journal of Public Health, 76*, 766–772.

Russell, L. B., Gold, M., Siegel, J. E., Daniels, N., & Weinstein, M. C. (1996). The role of cost-effectiveness analysis in health and medicine. *Journal of the American Medical Association, 276*, 1172–1177.

Selby, J. V., Fireman, B., Lundstrom, R. J., Swain, B. E., Truman, A. F., Wong, C. C., Froelicher, E. S., Barron, H.V., & Hlatky, M.A. (1996). Variation among hospitals in coronary angiography practices and outcomes after myocardial infarction in a large health maintenance organization. *New England Journal of Medicine, 335*, 1888–1896.

Sharpe, V. A., & Faden, A. I. (1996). Appropriateness in patient care: A new conceptual framework. *Milbank Quarterly, 74*, 115–138.

Starfield, B., Powe, N. R., Weiner, J. R., Stuart, M., Steinwachs, D., Scholle, S. H., & Gerstenberger, A. (1994). Costs vs. quality in different types of primary care settings. *Journal of the American Medical Association, 272*, 1903–1908.

Steinberg, E. P. (1993). Variations research: The physician perspective. *Medical Care, 31*(5 Supplement), YS86–YS88.

Stockwell, H., & Vayda, E. (1979). Variations in surgery in Ontario. *Medical Care, 17*, 390–396.

Volinn, E., Mayer, J., Diehr, P., Van Koevering, D., Connell, F. A., & Loeser, J. D. (1992). Small area analysis of surgery for low-back pain. *Spine, 17*, 575–579.

Watson, D. E., & Mathews, M. (1998). Economic evaluation of occupational therapy: Where are we at? *Canadian Journal of Occupational Therapy, 65*, 160–167.

Weiner, J. P., Starfield, B. H., Powe, N. R., Stuart, M. E., & Steinwachs, D. M. (1996). Ambulatory care practice variation within a Medicaid program. *Health Services Research, 30*, 751–770.

Wennberg, J. E., & Gittelsohn, A. (1973). Small area variations in health care delivery. *Science, 182*, 1102–1182.

White House Domestic Policy Council. (1993). *Health security: The President's report to the American people*. Washington, DC: Author.

2
Evaluating Clinical Services

The goal of service delivery is not quality alone, but also value. Quality of care is assumed, and value is expected. (Foto, 1997, p. 88)

Learning Objectives

- Explain the influence of the structure, process, and outcomes of care to service quality.
- Define and give examples of the structure, process, and outcome of care.
- Define the similarities and differences among clinical, program, and economic evaluations.
- Illustrate and describe a conceptual framework for understanding the components of an economic evaluation.
- List and briefly describe five different types of economic evaluation.

Quality of care has traditionally been defined and assessed using the classic triad of structure, process, and outcome (Donabedian, 1966). The structure of care pertains to the resource contributions required to provide care as well as the social, economic, and political context of service delivery. *Structure* refers to the "relatively stable characteristics of the provider, of the tools and resources they have at their disposal, and of the physical and organizational settings in which they work" (Donabedian, 1980, p. 81). The *process* of care represents the technical and humanistic profiles of caregivers or the actions, activities, and procedures that occur between service delivery and patients. The *outcome* of care refers to the results of the structure and process of care and represents the "change in a patient's current and future health that can be attributed to antecedent health care" (Donabedian, 1980, p. 82). Outcomes are the end results or products of care and describe what happened to the service recipient after he or she receives care. "A good outcome is a result that achieves the goal of the process" (Davies et al., 1994, p. 7).

Any comprehensive evaluation of the quality of a health service requires a complete accounting and understanding of the linkages, interplay, and causal relationships among the structure, process, and outcome of care (Donabedian, 1966; 1980). Figure 1 provides a framework that illustrates these components. The most common methods used to assess and monitor the quality of care include clinical evaluation, program evaluation, and economic evaluation.

Clinical Evaluations

Investigators who conduct clinical evaluations attempt to assess the linkages between the process of care to positive and negative outcomes to identify what works best for certain persons (Basinski et al., 1992; Guadagnoli, & McNeil, 1994). These investigators often test hypotheses regarding associations between clinical services that have been provided and changes in a person's health status to assess the type of relationships and the magnitude of associations between health services and outcomes and to establish causal relationships (Lohr, 1988). There are two types of clinical evaluations: (a) efficacy and (b) effectiveness assessments. Research on the efficacy of an intervention is conducted to determine the level of benefit that can be expected when interventions or services are provided by the most skilled practitioners under ideal or well-controlled conditions. These clinical studies use tightly defined sampling strategies and strict intervention protocols. By comparison, effectiveness research is conducted to determine the level of benefit that can be expected when average practitioners provide a health service to typical recipients under ordinary circumstances (Lohr, 1988; Office of Technology Assessment, 1978). Effectiveness research represents the first step in conducting evaluations of the costs and outcomes of care, and the methods used to conduct these assessments are summarized in chapter 6.

Program Evaluations

Investigators who implement program evaluations attempt to appraise, document, and describe the structure, process, and outcome of care for a specific service or intervention. These investigators systematically collect and analyze information about a service to guide judgments or decisions regarding that intervention. The purposes of these evaluations are to establish the merit, worth, or quality of programs by assessing the degree to which services were implemented as designed and to investigate the effectiveness, efficiency, and relevance of the service (Ferris et al., 1992; Scriven, 1994). Program evaluations include need, process, and outcome assessments. The main difference between program and clinical evaluations is that the former tends to focus on the attainment of programmatic objectives, whereas the latter concentrates on the effects of specific interventions. Both evaluations are used to assess and improve the quality of care provided to service recipients.

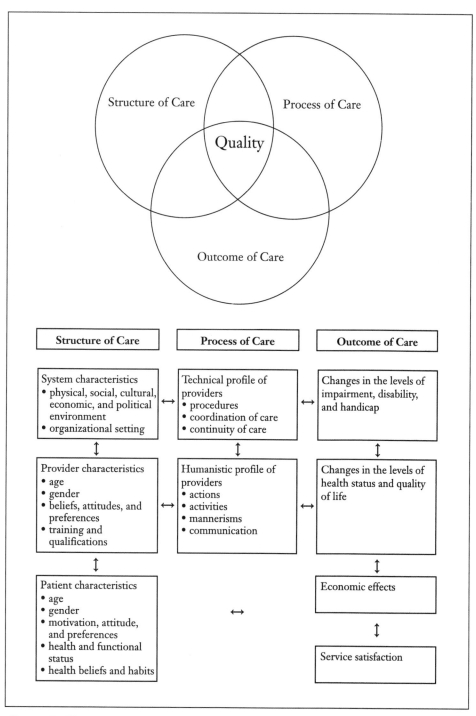

Figure 1. The structure, process, and outcome of care. Adapted from "The Medical Outcomes Study: An Application of Methods for Monitoring the Results of Medical Care," by Tarlov et al., 1989, *Journal of the American Medical Association, 262,* pp. 925–930. Copyright 1989, American Medical Association. Adapted with permission.

Economic Evaluations

Economic evaluations offer investigators a systematic method to appraise the costs and outcomes of various health services. Investigators who conduct these assessments describe and may compare the structure of care (i.e., resource contributions or costs) and outcomes (i.e., clinical effectiveness) of different programs or therapeutic interventions to determine the relative value of each service. In this context, the term *value* refers to relative worth, utility, or importance of different service options. Although two or more services must be compared to assess the "relative value" of an intervention, one of these comparisons could be the "no service" alternative, which is equivalent to the use of a control group in experimental research. Economic evaluations can be used for quality assurance purposes, but initiatives to improve the quality of various health interventions require a greater understanding of the structure and process of care and the linkages between these components (Russell, Gold, Siegel, Daniels, & Weinstein, 1996).

Conceptual Framework

Figure 2 provides a conceptual framework to illustrate the components of an economic evaluation. The costs and outcomes of a health service, program, intervention, or product can be considered from the vantage point of society, the health sector, or consumers. The perspective used to conduct an evaluation is particularly important to determine in the planning stages as it plays a crucial role in determining the most relevant costs and outcomes to include in the assessment. Evaluations that are conducted from the same perspective as the audience for which they are intended are more likely to be useful (Stoddart, 1982).

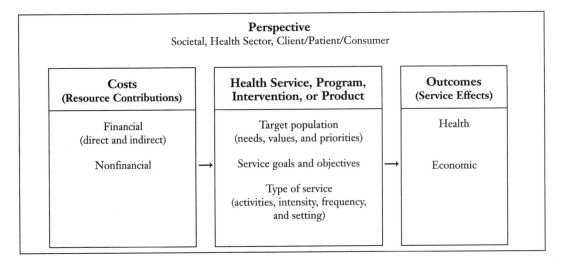

Figure 2. The components of an economic evaluation.

An evaluation that is conducted from the societal perspective considers the effect of the intervention on everyone and includes all of the costs and health outcomes that flow from it—regardless of whom experiences the effects (Russell, Siegel, et al., 1996). Although the societal perspective has been recommended as the optimal viewpoint for a cost-effectiveness analysis (Russell, Gold, et al., 1996), the completion of an assessment from this vantage point is complex and time consuming.

Evaluations can also be conducted from the perspective of stakeholders in the health sector such as the payers or health care providers, and most of the assessments that have been published in the literature have been conducted from these viewpoints. Analyses can be conducted from the standpoint of patients, clients, or consumers. When evaluations are carried out from viewpoints other than the societal perspective, some costs and outcomes can be omitted if they are not of interest to the audience who will be using the assessment (Russell, Siegel, et al., 1996). For example, investigators who conduct an analysis of an outpatient program from the perspective of the payer might not include costs such as out-of-pocket expenses paid by service recipients. However, these costs would be relevant if the evaluation was conducted from the viewpoint of consumers.

All health service evaluations should provide the audience of the assessment report with a detailed description of the service, program, intervention, or product. This narrative should include details regarding the target population and their needs, values, and priorities. If this population differs significantly from the characteristics of persons who actually use the service, the profile of these persons must also be documented. The goals and objectives of the service should be outlined, and a more detailed description of the activities, intensity, frequency, duration, and setting of the service should be included. This information serves three purposes: (a) the process of compiling this profile requires that investigators communicate with a variety of personnel to thoroughly understand the health service, (b) the inclusion of this profile in the assessment report ensures that the audience of this document understands the service being evaluated, and (c) this profile helps persons who read the report to make judgments regarding the potential to generalize the evaluation results to similar services.

All health services require resource contributions (i.e., the cost of providing a service) and produce an outcome (i.e., service effects or consequences). The various resource contributions that are required to produce and consume a service can be classified into financial and nonfinancial costs. The outcomes of the service can be classified into health or economic effects. For example, from the societal viewpoint all direct health care expenditures (i.e., financial costs) and the costs associated with patients' time (i.e., nonfinancial costs) are relevant and should be included in an analysis. The pertinent outcomes to include in this context are all improvements in impairments, disabilities, handicaps, and health-related quality of life (i.e., health effects) as well as alterations in future employ-ment earnings of service recipients (i.e., economic effects). Strategies that can be used to identify, measure, and value the costs and outcomes of a ser-vice from each viewpoint are described in more detail in other chapters.

Types of Economic Evaluation

There are five different types of economic evaluation: (a) cost-consequence, (b) cost-minimization, (c) cost-effectiveness, (d) cost-utility, and (e) cost-benefit analyses (Canadian Coordinating Office for Health Technology Assessment, 1997; Drummond, O'Brien, Stoddart, & Torrance, 1997). A summary of these different analytical approaches is provided in Table 1.

A cost-consequence analysis can be used to describe a health service or compare two or more health interventions in terms of their costs and outcomes. This type of analysis requires that investigators provide a descriptive profile of the costs (e.g., hospital costs, drug costs, out-of-pocket expenses, intangible costs such as patient time) and outcomes (e.g., health effects) of the intervention. The weighting or relative importance of different costs and outcomes is left to the user of the evaluation. This type of analysis is based on the premise that users can, and should, make the value judgment trade-off necessary to integrate a disparate list of pros and cons (Torrance, Siegel, & Luce, 1996).

Feldman, Latimer, and Davidson (1996) conducted a cost-consequences analysis when they evaluated the costs and consequences of providing home care services by way of a cluster care program versus a traditional model of service delivery. These investigators described and compared the costs, mortality, functional status, depressive symptoms, and service satisfaction of persons who received the two different models of home-based services. Hughes, Manheim, Edelman, and Conrad (1987) con-ducted a cost-consequences analysis when they evaluated the costs and consequences of rendering versus not providing long-term home care. These investigators described and compared the costs and institutional admission rates between these two groups. The concepts, principles, and methods guiding this type of evaluation are described in more detail in chapter 4.

A cost-minimization analysis can be used when investigators want to identify the least costly intervention when two or more services produce equivalent outcomes. Evidence that each service provides comparable out-comes must be demonstrated from either the literature or tested as part of the analysis. These evaluations assist in the identification of the most effi-cient means of attaining desired outcomes (Elixhauser, Luce, Taylor, & Reblando, 1993).

Trahey (1991) conducted a cost-minimization analysis when compar-ing the effect of providing occupational therapy in group versus individual

Table I
Summary of Measures and Results of Economic Evaluations

| Type of Evaluation | Measurement Unit | | Presentation of Results |
	Cost of Service	Consequences	
Cost-minimization	Net financial costs	Evidence of equivalent consequences	Cost per alternative
Cost-consequence	Different types of costs	Describe different types of health and economic consequences	Descriptive summary for each alternative
Cost-effectiveness	Net or incremental financial costs	Degree of: Impairment Disability Handicap Satisfaction	Cost per change in Impairment Disability Handicap Cost per unit of satisfaction
Cost-utility	Net financial costs	Health status Healthy years QALY	Cost per change in health status Cost per healthy year Cost per QALY
Cost-benefit	Net financial costs	Net financial benefits	Ratio of cost of service to cost of consequence Net cost or net benefit

Note. QALY = quality adjusted life year. Adapted from "Economic Evaluation of Occupational Therapy: Where Are We At?" by D. Watson & M. Mathews, 1998. *Canadian Journal of Occupational Therapy, 65*, p. 162. Copyright 1998 by the Canadian Association of Occupational Therapists (CAOT). Reproduced with permission of CAOT Publications.

treatment sessions for persons who had a total hip replacement. No significant differences where found in the functional performance of participants who received the two types of care. However, group therapy was much less costly than individualized services. Johnston and Miller (1986) also conducted a cost-minimization analysis when they evaluated the Health Care Financing Administration (HCFA) requirement that persons who obtain inpatient rehabilitation through the Medicare program receive at least 3 hr of therapy every day. Patients who received rehabilitation services before the HCFA regulation were compared with patients who received care after the regulation. No significant differences were found in functional outcomes or discharge destinations between the two groups, but there were significant differences in terms of therapy intensity and service costs. Most service evaluations are initially designed as cost-effectiveness studies but are reclassified as cost-minimization analyses when investigators determine that the interventions produce the same or similar outcomes.

A cost-effectiveness analysis requires that investigators describe and compare the costs and outcomes of two or more health services. These evaluations require that services produce the same type of outcome so that the results of the assessment can be used to compare these interventions in terms of costs per unit of health effect or health effects per unit of cost (Drummond et al., 1997; Russell, Siegel, et al., 1996). Rizzo, Baker, McAvay, and Tinetti (1996) conducted a cost-effectiveness analysis when they evaluated and compared the costs and effectiveness of providing a multifactorial, targeted fall prevention program to persons deemed at risk for fall-related injuries. These evaluators calculated the costs per fall prevented for persons who received the intervention. The concepts, principles, and methods guiding this type of evaluation are described in more detail in chapter 4.

A cost-utility analysis requires that costs be related to the outcomes of a service where the effectiveness of an intervention is determined by assessing both health status and the value of that status to the client. Almost 2 decades ago Boyle, Torrance, Sinclair, and Horwood (1983) conducted a cost-utility analysis when they compared the delivery of neonatal intensive care to nonintensive care to very low birth weight (VLBW) infants. These investigators calculated the cost per life year gained and cost per quality-adjusted life year (QALY) for each intervention. A QALY is a value that has been used by researchers to assess the effects of services on the quantity and quality of life (Weinstein & Stason, 1977). The concepts, principles, and methods guiding this type of evaluation are described in more detail in chapter 5.

A cost-benefit analysis requires that investigators measure both the cost and outcomes of health services using monetary figures. The results of this type of analysis can be presented in terms of a ratio (e.g., financial costs to financial benefits) or as a sum of costs and benefits (e.g., net financial effect or value). Boyle et al. (1983) conducted a cost-benefit analysis of offering neonatal intensive care versus nonintensive care to VLBW infants. The net financial effect of intensive care was calculated by subtracting the additional cost of this intervention from the extra lifetime earnings that would accrue to patients who received this service. This analysis helped the investigators to compute the net financial value of offering intensive care to these at-risk neonates. The concepts, principles, and methods guiding this type of evaluation are described in more detail in chapter 5.

Before conducting any economic evaluation, investigators should review the literature to determine whether research has demonstrated that the health service is effective or whether there is evidence that the services being compared are equally effective. The effectiveness of the service should be established before any assessment of costs, as it would be inappropriate and wasteful to evaluate the cost of providing ineffective services (Drummond et al., 1997). In addition, services that are equally effective can be assessed using a cost-minimization approach. This type of evaluation is less expensive to conduct than other analyses, as investigators only have to calculate resource costs and not outcomes. Some of the advantages and disadvantages of these economic evaluation methods are summarized in Table 2.

Many investigators use more than one type of economic evaluation when assessing the relative value of an intervention. For example, Rizzo et al. (1996) compared a fall prevention program to the delivery of no intervention by conducting a cost-effectiveness analysis of the costs per fall prevented and a cost-benefit analysis from the payer perspective of the net financial effect of offering this intervention. Boyle et al. (1983) compared the provision of intensive versus nonintensive care to neonates by conducting a cost-utility analysis to calculate the cost per QALY of providing intensive intervention and a cost-benefit analysis to calculate the net financial effect of offering this intervention.

Summary

Although quality of care is a multidimensional and complex concept, any evaluation of a health service requires that investigators recognize the different components of care and the linkages between structure, process, and outcome. Whereas clinical and program evaluations focus on the identification and description of the effectiveness of a specific intervention or program, economic evaluations describe and compare the costs and outcomes of health services. Although these assessments are often interpreted as cost-containment initiatives, their purpose is to provide decision makers with information regarding the costs and outcomes of different health services so that decisions regarding resource allocation can be based

Table 2
Summary of the Strengths and Weaknesses of Different Types of Economic Evaluations

Evaluation Approach	Strengths	Weaknesses
Cost-minimization	Determines least costly of equally effective alternatives The results are easily understood by audiences	Can only be used to compare services with the same outcomes as service alternatives must be equally effective Cannot be used to determine the relative effectiveness of different services
Cost-consequence	The results are easily understood by audiences Helps comparisons between services with different outcomes	Service costs and consequences are only described and not weighted in terms of their importance
Cost-effectiveness	Costs related to single, common health effects Measure impairments, disabilities, and handicaps	Cannot be used to compare services that affect different or multiple domains of health Does not include an assessment of service recipients preferences for different health outcomes Cannot be used to assess the economic or financial effect of a service on recipients
Cost-utility	Measures quantity and health-related quality of life Helps comparisons between services with different outcomes	May not measure clinically significant changes in impairments and disabilities QALY may have limited generalizability
Cost-benefit	Summarizes costs and outcomes using a ratio Provides information on the net financial effect of a service Helps comparisons between services with different outcomes	Decision makers may be uncomfortable with monetary valuation of health outcomes Limits measurement to costs and outcomes that can be easily valued in financial figures

Note. QALY = quality adjusted life year.

on research evidence. The specific costs (i.e., financial and nonfinancial) and outcomes (i.e., health and economic) that are important to include in the assessment are dependent on the viewpoint of the analysis. Evaluations conducted from the same perspective as the audience for which the final report is prepared are more likely to be useful. Different types of economic evaluation will be explained in more detail in subsequent chapters. ❖

Practice Exercises

Refer to Appendix D for responses to all exercise questions.

1. Tinetti et al. (1994) conducted an evaluation of an intervention program that was designed to reduce the frequency of falls among high-risk, elderly persons who lived in the community. These investigators determined that the intervention was associated with a 30% reduction in the rate of falls. What type of evaluation was conducted?

2. Rizzo, Baker, McAvay, and Tinetti (1996) conducted an evaluation of an intervention program that was designed to reduce the frequency of falls among high-risk, elderly persons who lived in the community. These investigators calculated the mean, median, and range of intervention costs per participant and compared this to the financial savings that would accrue from reductions in expenses from hospital, nursing home, and home health services secondary to the prevention of fall-related injuries. What type of evaluation was conducted?

3. Gold, Gafni, Nelligan, and Millson (1997) conducted an evaluation of a needle exchange program that was designed to prevent HIV transmission among persons who shared injection needles. These investigators calculated the cost per case prevented and the net cost savings of this intervention strategy. Net cost savings was calculated by subtracting intervention costs from the lifetime health care costs of treating an AIDS patient. What type of evaluation was conducted?

4. Rissanen et al. (1997) conducted an evaluation of hip and knee replacement surgery. These investigators calculated the health and medical care costs of providing surgery to changes in functional status and quality of life following this intervention and compared these outcomes for patients in three different age groups (i.e., less than 60 years of age, 61–70 years of age, more than 70 years of age). What type of evaluation was conducted?

5. Oldridge et al. (1993) conducted an evaluation of a cardiac rehabilitation program that was offered to persons who had experienced an acute myocardial infarction. These investigators determined the incremental cost of offering the intervention and calculated the cost per quality adjusted life year for this program. What type of evaluation was conducted?

6. Clark et al. (1997) evaluated a preventative health program that was designed to mitigate the health risks of older adulthood. These investigators determined that occupational therapy services enhanced the health status of those who received preventative intervention. What type of evaluation was conducted?

References

Basinski, A., Naylor, C. D., Ferris, L. E., Williams, J. I., Llewellyn-Thomas, H. A., & Cohen, M. M. (1992). Quality of care: What is quality and how can it be measured? *Canadian Medical Association Journal, 146*(12), 2153–2158.

Boyle, M. H., Torrance, G. W., Sinclair, J. C., & Horwood, S. P. (1983). Economic evaluation of neonatal intensive care of very-low-birth-weight infants. *New England Journal of Medicine, 308,* 1330–1337.

Canadian Coordinating Office for Health Technology Assessment. (1997). *Guidelines for economic evaluation of pharmaceuticals: Canada* (2nd ed.). Ottawa, Ontario Canada: Author.

Clark, F., Azen, S. P., Zemke, R., Jackson, J., Carlson, M., Mandel, D., Hay, J., Josephson, K., Cherry, B., Hessel, C., Palmer, J., & Lipson, L. (1997). Occupational therapy for independent living older adults: A randomized controlled trial. *Journal of the American Medical Association, 278,* 1321–1326.

Davies, A. R., Thomas Doyle, M. A., Lansky, D., Rutt, W., Orsolits Stevic, M., & Doyle, J. B. (1994). Outcome assessment in clinical settings: A consensus statement on principles and best practices in project management. *Journal on Quality Improvement, 20*(1), 6–16.

Donabedian, A. (1966). Evaluating the quality of medical care. *Milbank Memorial Fund Quarterly, 44,* 166–206.

Donabedian, A. (1980). *Explorations in quality assessment and monitoring: The definitions of quality and approaches to its assessment* (Vol.1). Ann Arbor, Michigan: Health Administration Press.

Drummond, M. F., O'Brien, B. J., Stoddart, G. L., & Torrance, G. (1997). *Methods for the economic evaluation of health care programmes* (2nd ed.). Oxford, UK: Oxford University Press.

Elixhauser, A., Luce, B. R., Taylor, W. R., & Reblando, J. (1993). Health care CBA/CEA: An update on the growth and composition of the literature. *Medical Care, 31*(7 Supplement), JS1–JS11.

Feldman, P. H., Latimer, E., & Davidson, H. (1996). Medicaid-funded home care for the frail elderly and disabled: Evaluating the cost savings and outcomes of a service delivery reform. *Health Services Research, 31,* 489–508.

Ferris, L. E., Naylor, C. D., Basinski, A. S. H., Williams, J. I., Llewellyn-Thomas, H. A., & Cohen, M. M. (1992). Program evaluation in health care. *Canadian Medical Association Journal, 146,* 1301–1304.

Foto, M. (1997). Nationally Speaking—Preparing occupational therapists for the year 2000: The impact of managed care on education and training. *American Journal of Occupational Therapy, 51,* 88–90.

Gold, M., Gafni, A., Nelligan, P., & Millson, P. (1997). Needle exchange programs: An economic evaluation of a local experience. *Canadian Medical Association Journal, 157*, 255–262.

Guadagnoli, E., & McNeil, B. J. (1994). Outcomes research: Hope for the future or the latest rage? *Inquiry, 31*, 14–24.

Hughes, S. L., Manheim, L. M., Edelman, P. L., & Conrad, K. J. (1987). Impact of long-term home care on hospital and nursing home use and cost. *Health Services Research, 22*(1), 19–47.

Johnston, M. V., & Miller, L. S. (1986). Cost-effectiveness of the Medicare three-hour regulation: Physical plus occupational therapy. *Archives of Physical Medicine and Rehabilitation, 67*, 581–585.

Lohr, K. N. (1988). Outcomes measurement: Concepts and questions. *Inquiry, 25*, 37–50.

Office of Technology Assessment. (1978). *Assessing the efficacy and safety of medical technologies*. Washington, DC: Congress of the United States, Office of Technology Assessment. OTA–H–75.

Oldridge, N., Furlong, W., Fenny, D., Torrance, G., Guyatt, G., Crowe, J., & Jones, N. (1993). Economic evaluation of cardiac rehabilitation soon after acute myocardial infarction. *American Journal of Cardiology, 72*, 154–161.

Rissanen, P., Aro, P., Sintonen, H., Asikainen, K., Slätis, P., & Paavolainen, P. (1997). Costs and cost-effectiveness in hip and knee replacements: A prospective study. *International Journal of Technology Assessment in Health Care, 13*, 575–588.

Rizzo, J. A., Baker, D. I., McAvay, G., & Tinetti, M. E. (1996). The cost-effectiveness of a multifactorial targeted prevention program for falls among community elderly persons. *Medical Care, 34*, 954–969.

Russell, L. B., Gold, M., Siegel, J. E., Daniels, N., & Weinstein, M. C. (1996). The role of cost-effectiveness analysis in health and medicine. *Journal of the American Medical Association, 276*, 1172–1177.

Russell, L. B., Siegel, J. E., Daniels, N., Gold, M. R., Luce, B. R., & Mandelblatt, J. S. (1996). Cost-effectiveness analysis as a guide to resource allocation in health: Roles and limitations. In M. R. Gold, J. E. Siegel, L. B. Russell, & M. C. Weinstein (Eds.), *Cost-effectiveness in health and medicine* (pp. 3–24). New York: Oxford University Press.

Scriven, M. (1994). The fine line between evaluation and explanation. *Evaluation Practice, 15*(1) 75–77.

Stoddart, G. L. (1982). Economic evaluation methods and health policy. *Evaluation and the Health Professions, 5*, 393–414.

Tarlov, A. R., Ware, J. E., Greenfield, S., Nelson, E. C., Perrin, E., & Zubkoff, M. (1989). The medical outcomes study: An application of methods for monitoring the results of medical care. *Journal of the American Medical Association, 262*, 925–930.

Tinnetti, M. E., Baker, D. I., McAvay, G., Claus, E. B., Garrett, P., Gottschalk, M., Koch, M. L., Trainor, K., & Horwitz, R. I. (1994). A multifactorial intervention to reduce the risk of falling among elderly people living in the community. *New England Journal of Medicine, 331*, 821–827.

Torrance, G. W., Siegel, J. E., & Luce, B. R. (1996). Framing and designing the cost-effectiveness analysis. In M. R. Gold, J. E. Siegel, L. B. Russell, & M. C. Weinstein (Eds.), *Cost-effectiveness in health and medicine* (pp. 54–81). New York: Oxford University Press.

Trahey, P. J. (1991). A comparison of the cost-effectiveness of two types of occupational therapy services. *American Journal of Occupational Therapy, 45*, 397–400.

Watson, D., & Mathews, M. (1998). Economic evaluation of occupational therapy: Where are we at? *Canadian Journal of Occupational Therapy, 65*, 160–167.

Weinstein, M. C., & Stason, W. B. (1977). Foundations of cost-effectiveness analysis for health and medical practices. *New England Journal of Medicine, 296*, 716–721.

Learning Resources

Program Evaluation

Forer, S. (1996). *Outcome management and program evaluation made easy: A toolkit for occupational therapy practitioners*. Bethesda, MD: American Occupational Therapy Association.

Green, L. W., & Lewis, F. M. (1986). *Measurement and evaluation in health education and health promotion*. Palo Alto, CA: Mayfield.

Rossi, P. H., & Freeman, H. E. (1989). *Evaluation: A systematic approach* (4th ed.). Newbury Park, CA: Sage.

Clinical Evaluation

Campbell, D. T., & Stanley, J. C. (1966). *Experimental and quasi-experimental designs for research*. Skokie, IL: Rand McNally.

Cook, T. D., & Campbell, D. T. (1979). *Quasi-experimentation: Design and analysis issues for field settings*. Boston: Houghton Mifflin.

Economic Evaluation

Canadian Coordinating Office for Health Technology Assessment. (1997). *Guidelines for economic evaluation of pharmaceuticals: Canada* (2nd ed.). Ottawa, Ontario, Canada: Author.

Drummond, M. F., O'Brien, B. J., Stoddart, G. L., & Torrance, G. (1997). *Methods for the economic evaluation of health care programmes* (2nd ed.). Oxford, UK: Oxford University Press.

Goeree, R. (Ed.). (1994). *Evaluation of programs for the treatment of schizophrenia: A health economic perspective*. Ottawa, Ontario, Canada: Health Canada.

Gold, M. R., Siegel, J. E., Russell, L. B., & Weinstein, M. C. (1996). *Cost-effectiveness in health and medicine*. New York: Oxford University Press.

Johannesson, M. (1996). *Theory and methods of economic evaluation of health care*. Dordrecht, The Netherlands: Kluwer Academic Publishers.

Russell, L., Gold, M., Siegel, J. E., Daniels, N., & Weinstein, M. C. (1996). The role of cost-effectiveness analysis in health and medicine. *Journal of the American Medical Association, 276*, 1172–1177.

Sloan, F. A. (1995). *Valuing health care: Costs, benefits, and effectiveness of pharmaceuticals and other medical technologies*. New York: Cambridge University Press.

Section II

Determining the Value of Clinical Services

3
Designing and Managing an Evaluation

Occupational therapy must rise to a new level of sophistication in articulating *and* demonstrating *why our involvement with the complex challenges of daily living in a modern age is so critical.* (Wood, 1998, p. 406)

Learning Objectives
- Describe the steps involved in designing an evaluation project.
- Identify some of the challenges to successfully managing an evaluation.

Investigators who are interested in evaluating specific rehabilitation services are faced with the task of designing and managing a project that will provide valuable information to answer very complex questions such as: Is the health service effective at promoting desirable outcomes? How much does a service cost? How valuable is the service in comparison to an alternative intervention? Are we offering or receiving good value for our investment?

Projects that are well planned and managed help investigators to obtain reliable and valid information and make recommendations that are valued by the audience for whom the evaluation report is targeted. In addition, these projects are more likely to be completed in a timely fashion than evaluations that are not appropriately managed. This chapter outlines a series of questions that investigators should consider when initiating and implementing an evaluation. These probe questions are listed in Table 3.

Designing and implementing an evaluation is an iterative process. Determinations made at the beginning of the process must be reviewed when additional decisions are made, as any single decision will influence

Table 3
Probe Questions To Assist Investigators in Designing and Managing an Economic Evaluation

Study Design

What is the purpose of the evaluation?

Why is the research question important?

Who is the audience? What is the study perspective?

What are the most important and relevant costs and outcomes?

What type of analysis will be performed?

What have other studies found?

What type of research design will be used?

Who is the target audience of the health service? Who are the service recipients, and how will these participants be recruited?

Is the study feasible?

Project Management

Who designs and manages the study?

How will the data be collected, managed, and stored?

How will confidentiality be maintained? Are there ethical issues to address?

How much will it cost? Who will fund the project?

What are the time lines?

How will the results be disseminated?

other components of the investigation. The goal of this process is to collect data that can be used to answer a specific research question and to implement an evaluation that has internal validity. *Internal validity* refers to the extent to which costs and outcomes are attributable to the service rather than competing explanations (Shortell & Richardson, 1978).

Designing an Evaluation

What Is the Purpose of the Evaluation?

The first step in designing an evaluation is to determine whether the analysis will be descriptive or comparative or both. Descriptive evaluations simply describe a service, whereas comparative evaluations require that a service be compared with the delivery of an alternative intervention or no intervention. If a descriptive evaluation is conducted, investigators describe the goals and objectives of the service, the population for whom the program was provided, the type of intervention offered, the resource contributions or the costs of providing and consuming the service, and the outcomes or effect of the service. These components of an evaluation are outlined in more detail in Figure 2 in chapter 2. When conducting a comparative evaluation, this type of information is provided for each service or type of intervention that will be investigated.

Comparative evaluations profile the costs and outcomes of two or more alternative services, and these assessments could include comparisons between variations of the same service, different interventions, and providing a health service versus not offering a health service. Assessing the relative value of a service that is offered in different intensities or settings is an example of the first type of comparative evaluation. Johnston and Miller (1986) conducted this type of assessment when they compared the costs and outcomes of providing intensive versus less intensive inpatient rehabilitation to seniors. Trahey (1991) also implemented this type of assessment when comparing the costs and outcomes of offering group versus individualized occupational therapy to persons who had a recent total hip replacement. Assessing the costs and outcomes of rendering different interventions to persons who have the same health problem is an example of the second type of comparative evaluation. Oldridge et al. (1993) conducted this type of assessment when they compared the costs and outcomes of two different approaches to cardiac rehabilitation. Assessing the costs and outcomes of providing versus not offering a service is an example of the last type of comparative evaluation. This strategy of comparing the delivery of a service with a "no service" alternative is equivalent to the use of a control group. Gold, Gafni, Nelligan, and Millson (1997) and Rizzo, Baker, McAvay, and Tinetti (1996) conducted this type of assessment when they compared the costs and outcomes of providing versus not offering preventative health programs.

Once investigators have determined whether they will conduct a descriptive or comparative evaluation, they must define an answerable research question (Drummond, O'Brien, Stoddart, & Torrance, 1997). This question should provide a brief description of the health service or interventions under investigation, specify the scope of the evaluation such as the population for whom the service was provided, define the perspective and time horizon of the analysis, and identify the relevant costs and outcomes. For example, rather than ask the question "Is a fall prevention program worth it?" investigators should pose the question: "From a payer perspective, is a prevention program that is designed to reduce the frequency of falls among high-risk elderly who live in the community preferable to the current approach of fracture management in terms of annual, net, and financial effect?" This was or would have been the type of research question asked by Rizzo et al. (1996) when they conducted a cost-benefit analysis of a fall-prevention program.

In summary, investigators should declare a research question that defines the purpose of the evaluation. This question should describe a service or identify the interventions being compared, outline the perspective and time horizon of the analysis, specify the scope of the investigation, and detail the costs and outcomes considered. The remainder of the probe questions in this section will offer information to assist investigators in validating or revising this research question.

Why Is the Research Question Important?

Studies that are valued by wide audiences address frequently encountered clinical issues, situations for which treatments are uncertain or disputed, or circumstances where innovative interventions have been proposed. Priority should be given to the clients, service settings, and domains of disability that are the focus of the majority of rehabilitation practitioners (Davies et al., 1994; Watson & Mathews, 1998). Health issues and problems with important consequences should be given higher priority than those with comparatively insignificant ones (Evidence-Based Care Resource Group, 1994b).

When assessing whether a research question warrants a full evaluation, investigators should consider the prevalence and incidence of the targeted health condition, the significance of the costs and outcomes of the service, the availability of other research evidence, and the likelihood that the evaluation results will influence the delivery or management of care. Like the health services and programs they are designed to assess, economic evaluations should provide valuable information at a reasonable cost. Trivial matters are not worth the effort or expense.

Who Is the Audience? What Is the Study Perspective?

It is essential that an initial assessment be conducted to evaluate the information needs and perspective of the intended audience of the evaluation report to understand the study's contribution to the decision-making process (Torrance, Siegel & Luce, 1996). Investigators who conduct relevant and valuable evaluations consider the social and political context of the health service and the influence of this environment on decision makers. By profiling this audience, investigators can determine the perspective that will be used in the analysis and identify the most important and relevant costs and outcomes. This information should then be used to validate or revise the research question. Chapter 9 offers more discussion on profiling the target audience of an evaluation report.

Evaluations that are conducted from the same viewpoint as the audience for which they are intended are more likely to be useful as these assessments include all of the costs and outcomes considered relevant by these persons (Stoddart, 1982). Although the societal perspective has been recommended as the optimal viewpoint of an economic evaluation (Russell, Gold, Siegel, Daniels, & Weinstein, 1996), the completion of an assessment from this perspective is complex and time consuming. Therefore, investigators who have published their results in the literature tend to assume the perspective of the payer or provider (Watson & Mathews, 1998).

What Are the Most Important and Relevant Costs and Outcomes?

The research question guiding the design of an evaluation should specify the costs and outcomes included in the analysis. The methods by which the most important and relevant costs and outcomes are identified, measured, and valued are described in subsequent chapters. Investigators should choose costs and outcomes that parallel the goals of the health services being evaluated and the information needs and preferences of the audience for whom the evaluation report is intended. If the costs and outcomes selected for inclusion in the evaluation are not congruent with the information needs of stakeholders, a rationale should be provided to resolve this discrepancy.

Once the most relevant costs and outcomes have been identified and operationally defined, a determination must be made as to how these dimensions will be measured and how this information will be collected. The goal of this process is to obtain accurate and complete information. Investigators should consider the level of training provided to persons who collect this data and attempt to measure their interrater reliability as this will ensure that the information obtained is of high quality.

Investigators may prefer to measure specific outcome variables using existing instruments (e.g., standardized assessments) or by creating new ones (e.g., customized questionnaires). It would seem that the most common mistakes made by investigators are to use an assessment tool with which they are familiar rather than spend the effort required to discover a more appropriate instrument or to develop and use a tool whose psychometric properties are unknown. Investigators who spend the time required to identify and learn a new instrument that was specifically designed to measure the outcome of interest are much better off than persons who develop or use a tool whose psychometric properties are unknown. Information that is collected from an inappropriate measurement tool is of little value.

The identification and selection of an appropriate measurement tool should be influenced by discussions with clinical practitioners, administrators, and other stakeholders as well as evidence regarding the psychometric qualities of the instrument. As outlined in chapter 6 the selection of an instrument to measure an outcome requires a consideration of the tool's sensibility, feasibility, reliability, validity, and responsiveness (Deyo et al., 1994). These dimensions of a measurement instrument are essential to producing findings that are statistically and clinically significant. Appendix A lists a number of assessments that have been used to measure specific rehabilitation outcomes. Law (1987) published an excellent article that provides information to assist clinicians in determining the scientific rigor and utility of a measurement instrument.

In summary, the research question should specify the costs and outcomes included in the analysis. Investigators must determine how information regarding these dimensions will be measured and collected. The psychometric properties of any instrument should be considered as well as the accuracy and completeness of information sources and the training and reliability of data collectors.

What Type of Analysis Will Be Performed?

There are five different types of economic evaluations described in the preceding chapter—cost-consequence, cost-minimization, cost-effectiveness, cost-utility, and cost-benefit analyses. Although these analytical methods all require that information be collected regarding resource inputs (i.e., the costs of providing a service), they differ primarily in the way they measure health and economic outcomes. Cost-consequence analyses can be used to describe and compare services that promote change in an array of health and economic domains. Cost-minimization assessments are used when the services being compared are not significantly different in terms of health and economic outcomes. However, cost-effectiveness analyses require that services be compared in terms of specific health outcomes such as changes in impairments, disabilities, and handicaps. Cost-utility analyses require that services be compared in terms of their effect on the quality and quantity of life. Cost-benefit analyses require that services be evaluated in terms of their net financial effect; intervention costs are compared with the monetary value of health and economic outcomes.

Investigators who want to evaluate a service that was designed to promote changes in multiple health and economic domains usually conduct a cost-consequences analysis. A cost-effectiveness analysis would be appropriate if the interventions being compared were designed to promote change in one or two domains of health. Economic outcomes are not included in this type of evaluation. A cost-effectiveness analysis would also be appropriate to use if an intervention was compared with the "no service" alternative and the outcome of interest was in a domain of health. Cost-benefit analyses would be appropriate to perform if the primary outcome of interest was economic and the purpose of the assessment was to determine the net financial effect of offering a service.

Investigators should determine the type of outcome that is appropriate to measure before deciding on the type of analysis that will be conducted. The most relevant and appropriate outcome to measure can be identified by reviewing the goals of the services being evaluated, discovering what outcomes are valued by the target audience of the evaluation report, and determining the type of outcome indicators that are currently collected by service delivery systems. It is hoped that these outcomes will be congruent with the stated goals of the intervention, but this is not always the case. For example, the clientele may value information regarding the effect of the service on health-related quality of life but the intervention may be designed to promote improvements at the organ system level. Although service recipients may have improvements in certain impairments, these changes may not translate into changes in the way these persons rate their overall quality of life.[1] This type of discrepancy should be discussed with service providers and persons who will receive the final evaluation report, as resolution is required before investigators can determine the most appropriate outcomes to include in the analysis. Investigators must consider what type of outcome information is currently available or what is feasible to obtain from service recipients for the purposes of the evaluation. A more thorough discussion of this topic is provided in chapter 6.

What Have Other Studies Found?

A literature review is important to conduct during the initial planning stages of an evaluation, when investigators need to enhance their understanding of a particular issue and capitalize on what others have previously done (Evidence-Based Care Resource Group, 1994a, Warwick & Lininger, 1975). This process helps investigators to become more informed about the results of similar evaluations, the strengths and weaknesses of relevant methodological approaches, the importance of certain costs and outcomes, and the psychometric soundness of potential measurement instruments. The experiences and thoughts of other investigators will assist in clarifying the nature and significance of the clinical problem and guide interpretation of the results of an evaluation (Abramson, 1990). This review should be an ongoing process that continues throughout the study.

The Learning Resources section of this chapter and chapter 6 provide information on how to conduct a systematic review of the literature. Journal publications, government documents, reports from health care organizations, and the Internet are all sources of information.

---

[1] Many different health-related quality of life measures are not sensitive enough to capture clinically significant changes at the organ system level.

What Type of Research Design Will Be Used?

The design of a study provides the road map for the evaluation and the analysis. This road map should be devised in the planning stages to avoid unexpected detours. Clinical evaluations that have the strongest methodological rigor have an experimental research design (i.e., randomized controlled trial). Participants in these studies are randomly selected from a target population and assigned to treatment and control groups. In addition, testers are trained, blinded, and randomly assigned to participants. In most clinical and rehabilitation settings the implementation of an experimental design is not viable, so investigators use observational or quasi-experimental research designs. Katz et al. (1995) wrote an excellent article regarding different research designs to assist rehabilitation practitioners in appraising and implementing clinical research.

Since the late 1970s there has been a movement toward appraising the quality of evidence on the effectiveness of health interventions. Basically, evidence is rated high quality if it has been derived from a randomized, controlled trial where participants are randomly recruited and assigned to treatment and control groups. Nonrandomized trials, controlled or cohort studies, case series, case-controlled or cross-sectional research designs are rated moderate quality. The expressed or written opinions of experts that are based on their experience, knowledge of the literature, and discussion with peers are rated low quality (Center for Evidence-Based Medicine, 1998; Guyatt et al., 1995; United States Preventive Services Task Force, 1993).

The most common research designs used in economic evaluations include the "one-shot" case study and the "one group" pretest–posttest design (Shortell & Richardson, 1978). The one-shot case study involves having participants complete a questionnaire after they have received an intervention. The one group pretest–posttest is also a popular research design that is used in clinical settings. This approach requires that investigators assess the degree of change in service recipients by assessing them before and after they receive care. The results obtained from the one-shot case study and the one group pretest–posttest may hold more validity if the same findings are evident when this research design is implemented with more than one cohort of service clientele or during multiple time periods.

There are alternative quasi-experimental research designs that have been used to evaluate health interventions such as the nonequivalent control group (i.e., selection of a second group that is as similar as possible to the treatment group) and the time series design (i.e., multiple measures before and after receiving an intervention) (Campbell & Stanley, 1966). When investigators compare two different services that are already being provided to determine the relative value of each approach, this type of research design is similar conceptually to the nonequivalent control group.

The research design used by investigators has a direct influence on the internal validity of the evaluation. *Internal validity* refers to the extent to which costs and outcomes are attributable to the service rather than competing explanations (Shortell & Richardson, 1978). Therefore, it is important to explicitly state the type of research design used, to understand the shortcomings inherent in different designs, and to acknowledge these limitations in the final report. A more thorough discussion on this topic is provided in chapter 8.

Who Is the Target Population of the Health Service? Who Are the Service Recipients, and How Will These Persons Be Recruited?

The characteristics of the population for whom the service is targeted and for whom the service is consumed should be specified as this may affect the design of the evaluation and the communication of results. Again, there should be congruence between the characteristics of the target population and those of service recipients, but this is not always the case. Occasionally, there may be discrepancies between these two groups. Although this is an important finding to bring to the attention of service providers and to document in the final report, the evaluation will ultimately be conducted using a sample or samples of persons to whom the service was provided.

Once the characteristics of service recipients have been specified, this information can then be used to establish explicit inclusion and exclusion criteria and to develop a means by which participants can be screened for their appropriateness in the evaluation. The sample of service recipients who are recruited should include persons who represent the average consumer. The inclusion of very high- or low-cost users or those who have very atypical outcomes may sway the results. A discussion regarding the inclusion of these "outliers" in the analysis is provided in chapter 8. Alternatively, it may be appropriate to compile different subgroups of service recipients as cost and outcome data should not be combined for different clienteles. When information is combined from a sample that is too heterogeneous it may be impossible to describe who benefits most from an intervention and who does not. For example, it may be appropriate when evaluating an acute stroke rehabilitation program to define three types of service recipients—persons who are recovering from a transcient ischemic attack, persons who have experienced their first stroke, and those who have had prior cerebral accidents or premorbid central nervous system disorders. The inclusion and exclusion criteria used to select participants for the evaluation should be explicitly stated in the assessment report.

Investigators must determine how participants will be recruited. Because it may be inappropriate or impossible to recruit all service recipients, a sampling strategy should be developed to establish a solid basis for generalizations about the target population (Warwick & Lininger, 1975).

The goal of this process is to recruit a sample of service recipients who are representative of users. There are a number of sampling strategies that can be used by investigators, but samples that are drawn using random or stratified random techniques are more representative and help evaluators to make more valid generalizations. However, many researchers tend to collect data from a cross-sectional cohort of service recipients as this sampling strategy is more easily recruited. However, these investigators must assume that this cohort is similar to service recipients who receive care at other times.

In quantitative studies, evaluators calculate sample sizes to ensure that data is collected from a sufficient number of service recipients to detect clinical and statistical differences between groups. Sample sizes are dependent on the type of research design, the frequency of occurrence of the outcome of interest, and the statistical analyses that will be conducted (Cohen, 1987; du V Florey, 1993). There is no sense in conducting an evaluation and then not having enough participants to adequately address the research question (Munro, 1992).

Once service recipients have been recruited for inclusion in the evaluation, information regarding their demographic, social, and health profiles should be collected. The data that is important to collect are the characteristics of these participants that might influence their costs and outcomes. Some of these variables might include chronological age, premorbid and initial functional status, previous medical history, and comorbidities. This descriptive profile helps investigators and readers of the final evaluation report to understand the context of the evaluation, assess how well the sample represents the population of service recipients and those for whom the services were targeted, and make judgments regarding the external validity of the study. *External validity* refers to the extent to which findings can be generalized to similar persons or comparable services (Shortell & Richardson, 1978). This information can be used by investigators to determine whether these variables should be included as covariates when conducting multivariate analysis. A discussion regarding the use of this data for risk adjustment is provided in chapter 8.

In summary, the evaluation report should provide a profile of the population for whom the service was targeted, outline the characteristics of typical service recipients, and describe the participants who were recruited for assessment. Any similarities and differences among these three groups should be discussed. The characteristics of participants in the evaluation that are important to profile include those that may have a direct or indirect effect their resource use and outcomes. Conducting an evaluation to assess the value of an intervention on an undefined group of persons may produce misleading and unreliable results.

Is the Study Feasible?

A pilot study may be appropriate to conduct to determine the feasibility of collecting cost and outcome data as well as demographic, social, and health information from participants. This process helps investigators to determine whether data can be collected in a timely and efficient manner (Davies et al., 1994). In addition, investigators have the opportunity to elicit reactions from service recipients, clinical practitioners, and other participants in the evaluation regarding their involvement in the assessment. This information can be used to determine whether modifications must be made to the research question or the assessment methodology.

Project Management

Who Designs and Manages the Study?

Most of the economic evaluations that have been published in the literature have been developed and implemented by multidisciplinary teams of persons as these analyses often require that investigators possess a variety of skills and knowledge. For example, project teams may include clinical practitioners, administrative managers, researchers, statisticians, accountants, and health economists. All successful projects have a coordinator who brings together persons who will make valuable contributions. He or she oversees the project and ensures that the evaluation is implemented as designed. The project coordinator may be one of the persons who proposed the study or he or she may be hired externally. It is important to note that more than one person should be responsible for planning and conducting the entire evaluation. Roles are routinely shared by various members of the evaluation team so as to capitalize on each person's expertise (Davies et al., 1994).

Lengthy and complex evaluations are successful when a person such as a reputable senior clinician or administrator champions the project. The project champion does not necessarily need to be a member of the team who plans and conducts the study, but he or she should be able to use their influence to ensure that the staff members of service providers participate in data collection. Investigators require the approval and support of many persons to be able to conduct the study. Department managers, senior administrators, clinical practitioners, support staff members, and funding sources should be informed about the purpose of the evaluation, consulted regarding its design and implementation, and kept abreast of important developments. These activities could be performed by the project coordinator or champion.

Evaluations that attempt to establish the effectiveness of an intervention using a rigorous research study require that someone on the team have an understanding of research design and inferential statistics.

Therefore, these teams should be provided with adequate statistical and data analysis support. In addition, evaluations that include a full cost assessment require that someone on the team have an understanding of finance and accounting. Consultants should be used during the planning and data analysis stages if members of the team do not have a strong background in these areas.

How Will the Data Be Collected, Managed, and Stored?

Collecting the right data, on the right persons, at the right time, is the greatest challenge and the chief objective of every evaluation (Davies et al., 1994). Investigators should use the following probes when planning the data collection process: what, when, where, how, and by whom. The type of data collected (i.e., what) is dependent on the research question but will include information on costs, outcomes, and the sociodemographic and health characteristics of participants. When and where this information is compiled as well as the method used to collect this data (i.e., how) will depend on the context of service delivery. The strategies used to compile information should suit the workflow and organization of the clinical setting. Protocols that are disruptive will not receive the full cooperation of staff members. Investigators will have to make determinations about who will collect information (i.e., by whom). Data collectors should be trained to standardize procedures and reduce potential sources of bias or error. Once information from participants is collected, this data must be reviewed to ensure they are complete and accurate.

Data analysis can be simplified if information is stored in a database, spreadsheet, or statistical software program. Investigators should design and format a database so that this information can be analyzed to answer specific research questions and to demonstrate the results of the evaluation. This requires a determination of when the data will be entered (e.g., in real time or delayed), how the data will be entered (e.g., manually or automated), who will enter the data (e.g., staff members), how personal identifiers will be used to maintain confidentiality, and how the data will be coded. Consultants are useful if investigators are not familiar with software programs for data entry and analysis.

How Will Confidentiality Be Maintained? Are There Ethical Issues To Address?

Evaluations that involve the compilation of information from service recipients and require that an intervention be altered for research purposes must be approved by ethics committees. These committees ensure that evaluations meet ethical standards and that the results obtained by investigators are worthy of the risks required of participants. Some ethics committees ensure that the design of the study will help investigators to appropriately answer the stated research question.

Throughout the planning stages of any evaluation, investigators should review the ethical standards of the health service organizations involved in the study, any sites from which data will be collected as well as the funding agency to ensure that the study is in compliance with these guidelines. The most common requirement is that investigators give an honest explanation of the purpose of the evaluation, provide a description of what the assessment entails, obtain informed consent from participants, and maintain confidentiality. Service recipients who contribute information for the sole purpose of the evaluation should be told that they are permitted to refuse to participate without prejudicing their treatment and may withdraw from participating in the project at any time.

How Much Will It Cost? Who Will Fund the Project?

The cost of conducting the evaluation should be considered very early in the planning process. The resources required to implement an evaluation will primarily be determined by whether the investigators will use information from the literature regarding effectiveness and resource use or conduct a clinical effectiveness study and a full cost assessment. Ultimately, investigators must work within a budget and determine whether the evaluation is worth the resources required for its implementation.

When developing a budget investigators must take into account the costs associated with the planning and implementation of the evaluation as well as the communication of results. It is important to incorporate the cost of having staff members collect information when this data is required solely for the purpose of the evaluation. If the information that will be used by investigators is collected by staff members during the delivery of routine care, the cost associated with this time is not relevant. Investigators should determine whether any funding agencies provide grants for health service evaluations, but it is important to determine whether the conditions imposed by these agencies influence the perspective or focus of the analysis.

What Are the Time Lines?

Evaluations that are completed in a timely fashion have likely been implemented according to a schedule set by investigators during the planning stages. Successful management of any project requires that deadlines be established for individual elements of a study as well as the overall evaluation. The cost and outcome variables that have been selected may dictate the time frame over which the study must be conducted, as long-term outcomes will require follow-up over lengthier periods of time. Time restraints imposed on a study may also influence the design of the evaluation and the communication of results. As with any complex project, expect and plan for unforeseen obstacles and delays.

How Will the Results Be Disseminated?

As outlined in chapter 9, a dissemination strategy should be developed during the planning phase of any evaluation. This strategy should consider the information needs and priorities of the audience for whom the report is prepared. Whereas a pilot study may be conducted to assess the feasibility of a research design, a communication strategy can also be field tested with various stakeholders for interpretive feedback. Persons and organizations who participated in various stages of the study may be interested in the findings and may be of assistance in providing feedback. Funding agencies often specify how and when results should be made available. ❖

Practice Exercises

You would like to conduct a comparative evaluation to assess the relative value of a fall prevention program that is targeted at the high-risk elderly in the community. This is the type of study that was conducted by Rizzo et al. (1996). Refer to Appendix D for responses to all exercise questions.

1. What are the two alternatives being compared?
2. What are the costs and outcomes of interest if the investigators conduct a cost-benefit analysis from the perspective of the payer?
3. Define a research question.

References

Abramson, J. H. (1990). *Survey methods in community medicine* (4th ed.). Edinburgh: Churchill Livingstone.

Campbell, D. T., & Stanley, J. C. (1966). *Experimental and quasi-experimental designs for research*. Skokie, IL: Rand McNally.

Center for Evidence-Based Medicine. (1998, September 17). Levels of evidence and grades of recommendations. [Announcement posted on the World Wide Web]. Oxford, England: Author. Retrieved January 8, 1999 from the World Wide Web: www.cebm.jr2.ox.ac.uk/docs/levels.html

Cohen, J. (1987). *Statistical power analysis for the behavioral sciences* (2nd ed.). Hillsdale, NJ: Lawrence Erlbaum.

Davies, A. R., Thomas Doyle, M. A., Lansky, D., Rutt, W., Orsolitis Stevic, M., & Doyle, J. B. (1994). Outcomes assessment in clinical settings: A consensus statement on principles and best practices in project management. *Journal on Quality Improvement, 20,* 1, 6–16.

Deyo, R.., Andersson, G., Bombardier, C., Cherkin, D. C., Kellerm R. B., Lee, C. K., Liang, M. H., Lipscomb, B., Shekelle, P., Spratt, K. F., Weinstein, J. N. (1994).

Outcome measures for studying patients with low back pain. *Spine*, 19, 2032S–2036S.

Drummond, M. F., O'Brien, B. J., Stoddart, G. L., & Torrance, G. (1997). *Methods for the economic evaluation of health care programmes* (2nd ed.). Oxford, UK: Oxford University Press.

du V Florey, C. (1993). Sample size for beginners. *British Medical Journal, 306*, 1181–1184.

Evidence-Based Care Resource Group. (1994a). Evidence-based care. Setting guidelines: How should we manage this problem? *Canadian Medical Association Journal, 150*, 1417–1423.

Evidence-Based Care Resource Group. (1994b). Evidenced-based care. Setting priorities: How important is this problem? *Canadian Medical Association Journal, 150*, 1249–1253.

Gold, M., Gafni, A., Nelligan, P., & Millson, P. (1997). Needle exchange programs: An economic evaluation of a local experience. *Canadian Medical Association Journal, 157*, 255–262.

Guyatt, G. H., Sackett, D. L., Sinclair, J. C., Hayward, R., Cook, D., & Cook, R. J. (1995). Users' guide to the medical literature: A method for grading health care recommendations. *Journal of the American Medical Association, 274*, 1800–1804.

Johnston, M.V., & Miller, L. S. (1986). Cost-effectiveness of the Medicare three-hour regulation: Physical plus occupational therapy. *Archives of Physical Medicine and Rehabilitation, 67*, 581–585.

Katz, R. T., Campagnolo, D. I., Goldberg, G., Parker, J. C., Pine, Z. M., & Whyte, J. (1995). Critical evaluation of clinical research. *American Journal of Physical Medicine and Rehabilitation, 76*, 82–93.

Law, M. (1987). Measurement in occupational therapy: Scientific criteria for evaluation. *Canadian Journal of Occupational Therapy, 54*, 133–138.

Munro, B. H. (1992). How many subjects are enough? *Clinical Nurse Specialist*, 20.

Oldridge, N., Furlong, W., Fenny, D., Torrance, G., Guyatt, G., Crowe, J., & Jones, N. (1993). Economic evaluation of cardiac rehabilitation soon after acute myocardial infarction. *American Journal of Cardiology, 72*, 154–161.

Rizzo, J. A., Baker, D. I., McAvay, G., & Tinetti, M. E. (1996). The cost-effectiveness of a multifactorial targeted prevention program for falls among community elderly persons. *Medical Care, 34*, 954–969.

Russell, L. B., Gold, M. R., Siegel, J. E., Daniels, N., & Weinstein, M. C. (1996). The role of cost-effectiveness analysis in health and medicine. *Journal of the American Medical Association, 276*, 1172–1177.

Shortell, S. M., & Richardson, W. C. (1978). *Health program evaluation*. St. Louis, MO: Mosby.

Stoddart, G. L. (1982). Economic evaluation methods and health policy. *Evaluation and the Health Professions, 5*, 393–414.

Torrance, G. W., Siegel, J. E., & Luce, B. R. (1996). Framing and designing the cost-effectiveness analysis. In M. R. Gold, J. E. Siegel, L. B. Russell, & M. C. Weinstein (Eds.), *Cost-effectiveness in health and medicine* (pp. 54–81). New York: Oxford University Press.

Trahey, P. J. (1991). A comparison of the cost-effectiveness of two types of occupational therapy services. *American Journal of Occupational Therapy, 45*, 397–400.

United States Preventative Services Task Force. (1993). Screening for adolescent idiopathic scoliosis: Review article. *Journal of the American Medical Association, 269*, 2667–2672.

Warwick, D., & Lininger, C. (1975). *The sample survey: Theory and practice.* New York: McGraw-Hill.

Watson, D. E., & Mathews, M. (1998). Economic evaluation of occupational therapy: Where are we at? *Canadian Journal of Occupational Therapy, 65*, 160–167.

Wood, W. (1998). Nationally Speaking—It is jump time for occupational therapy. *American Journal of Occupational Therapy, 52*, 403–411.

Learning Resources

Project Management

Davies, A. R., Thomas Doyle, M. A., Lansky, D., Rutt, W., Orsolitis Stevic, M., & Doyle, J. B. (1994). Outcomes assessment in clinical settings: A consensus statement on principles and best practices in project management. *Journal on Quality Improvement, 20*, 6–16.

Shea, M. P., & Lewko, J. H. (1995). Use of a stakeholder advisory group to facilitate utilization of evaluation results. *Canadian Journal of Program Evaluation, 10*, 159–162.

Weiss, C. H. (1987). Where politics and evaluation research meet. In D. J. Palumbo (Ed.), *The politics of program evaluation* (pp. 47–70). London: Sage.

Study Design

Torrance, G. W., Siegel, J. E., & Luce, B. R. (1996). Framing and designing the cost-effectiveness analysis. In M. R. Gold, J. E. Siegel, L. B. Russell, & M. C. Weinstein (Eds.), *Cost-effectiveness in health and medicine* (pp. 54–81). New York: Oxford University Press.

Systematic Reviews of the Literature

Bero, L., & Rennie, D. (1995). The Cochrane Collaboration: Preparing, maintaining and disseminating systematic reviews of the effects of health care. *Journal of the American Medical Association, 274*, 570–574.

Dickersin, K., Scherer, R., & Lefebrve, C. (1994). Identifying relevant studies for systematic reviews. *British Medical Journal, 309*, 1286–1291.

Findley, T. W., (1991). Research in physical medicine and rehabilitation: The conceptual review of the literature on how to read more articles than you ever want to see in your entire life. *American Journal of Physical Medicine and Rehabilitation, 70*, S17–S22.

Forchuk, C., & Roberts, J. (1993). How to critique qualitative research articles. *Canadian Journal of Nursing Research, 25*, 47–55.

Friede, A., Taylor, W. R., & Nadelman, L. (1993). On-line access to a cost-benefit/cost-effectiveness analysis bibliography via CDC WONDER. *Medical Care, 31*(7 Supplement), JS12–JS17.

Hayes, R., & McGrath, J. (1998). Evidence-based practice: The Cochrane Collaboration and occupational therapy. *Canadian Journal of Occupational Therapy, 65,* 144–151.

Katz, R. T., Campagnolo, D. I., Goldberg, G., Parker, J. C., Pine, Z. M., & Whyte, J. (1995). Critical evaluation of clinical research. *American Journal of Physical Medicine and Rehabilitation, 76,* 82–93.

Oxman, A. D. (Ed.). (1994). Section VI: Preparing and maintaining systematic reviews. In *The Cochrane Collaboration Handbook.* Oxford: Cochrane Collaboration. This document is available on the World Wide Web at http://hiru.mcmaster.ca/COCHRANE/handbook/default.htm

Oxman, A. D., & Guyatt, G. H. (1988). Guidelines for reading literature reviews. *Canadian Medical Association Journal, 138,* 697–703.

Pollock, N. (1998). Reflections on ... The Cochrane Collaboration. *Canadian Journal of Occupational Therapy, 65,* 168–170.

Shekelle, P. G., Andersson, G., Bombardier, C., Cherkin, D., Deyo, R., Keller, R., Lee, C., Liang, M., Lipscomb, B., Spratt, K., & Weinstein, J. (1994). A brief introduction to the critical reading of the clinical literature. *Spine, 19,* 2028S–2031S.

The Cochrane Library offers electronic access to high quality evidence regarding health care interventions. The Cochrane Library includes the *Cochrane Database on Systematic Reviews*, the *Cochrane Clinical Trials Register*, the *Cochrane Review Methodology Database*, and the *Database of Abstracts of Reviews of Effectiveness.* The *Cochrane Database of Systematic Reviews* is a popular source of reviews regarding the efficacy and effectiveness of health care interventions. It contains a collection of regularly updated, systematic reviews that are primarily based on randomized controlled trials. The *Cochrane Clinical Trials Register* is an electronic bibliography of controlled trials that have been identified by contributors to the Cochrane Collaboration. It contains research studies that are both published and not published and represents an unbiased source of data for systematic reviews. The *Cochrane Review Methodology Database* is an electronic database of publications regarding the methods by which research can be critically appraised and synthesized. The *Database of Abstracts of Reviews of Effectiveness* (DARE) includes structured abstracts of systematic reviews from around the world. This database is maintained by the National Health Service Centre for Reviews and Dissemination at the University of York in England. (See below for more details).

Access to The Cochrane Library is available through most university libraries. The CD-ROM version can be obtained by subscription from the BMJ Publishing Group. Hayes and McGrath (1998) and Pollock (1998) discussed the importance and utility of the Cochrane Database to occupational therapy. Refer to Bero and Rennie (1995) for more information on the Cochrane Collaboration. The Cochrane Collaboration site in the United States is at the University of Maryland School of Medicine, Department of Epidemiology and Preventative Medicine. Their World Wide Web site is at www.cochrane.org/

The National Health Service's (NHS) Centre for Reviews and Dissemination provides the results of systematic reviews and has the *Database of Abstracts of Reviews of Effectiveness* (DARE) and the *NHS Economic Evaluation Database*. Three electronic databases are available from the World Wide Web at www.york.ac.uk/inst/crd/

The Centers for Disease Control and Prevention (CDC) has developed an on-line bibliography on economic evaluations that have been conducted in the area of preventative health. This *Wide-ranging On-line Data for Epidemiologic Research* (CDC WONDER) is available to all health professionals at no cost (Friede, Taylor, & Nadelman, 1993).

The National Library of Medicine offers access to 16 electronic databases including MEDLINE© through their Internet Grateful Med (IGM). The Library has recently made its IGM training manual available in PDF, PostScript, and WordPerfect formats. This information is available on the World Wide Web at http://igm.nlm.nih.gov/

4

Cost-Consequence and Cost-Effectiveness Analyses

Patients are in the dark on most medical decisions, unaware of risks and benefits of alternative treatments or settings.... Making this information available would give consumers a way of knowing that the care they receive is high quality and cost-effective. (White House Domestic Policy Council, 1993)

Learning Objectives

- Define and describe cost-consequence and cost-effectiveness analyses.
- List the benefits and challenges of these two types of evaluation.

The ultimate goal of investigators who conduct evaluations to describe and compare the costs and outcomes of a health service is to provide decision makers with information regarding the relative value of these interventions. In this context, the term *value* refers to the relative worth, utility, or importance of a service in meeting specific health needs of a defined clientele. This chapter will focus on describing cost-consequence and cost-effectiveness analyses and outlining the benefits and challenges of these two methods.

Cost-consequence and cost-effectiveness analyses are the evaluation methods most commonly used to determine the value of clinical services and to provide decision makers with information regarding resource contributions and the outcomes of a service. Cost-consequence analyses describe the costs as well as the health and economic outcomes of one or more health services. By comparison, cost-effectiveness analyses describe the costs and health outcomes of two or more services so that these interventions can be directly compared. A summary of these two approaches to evaluation is provided in Table 4.

Table 4
Summary of Measures and Results of Cost-Consequence and Cost-Effectiveness Analyses

Type of Evaluation	Measurement Unit		Presentation of Results	Example Evaluation
	Cost of Service	Consequences		
Cost-consequence	Descriptive profile of the different types of intervention costs including start-up and ongoing expenditures	Descriptive profile of the different types of health and economic outcomes	Descriptive summary for each alternative	Feldman, Latimer, and Davidson (1996) compared the costs and consequences of delivering home care services according to a cluster care program versus a traditional model of service delivery.
Cost-effectiveness	Total or incremental costs including start-up and ongoing expenditures	Total or incremental changes in health such as changes in the level of impairment, disability, and handicap Satisfaction	Cost per unit of change in health such as alterations in impairment, disability, and handicap Cost per unit of satisfaction Cost-effectiveness ratio	Rizzo, Baker, McAvay, and Tinetti (1996) compared the costs and effectiveness of delivering a multi-factorial fall prevention intervention program with no intervention. These evaluators compared the services on the basis of costs per fall prevented.

Note. Adapted from "Economic Evaluation of Occupational Therapy: Where Are We At?" by D. Watson & M. Mathews, 1998. *Canadian Journal of Occupational Therapy*, 65, p. 162. Copyright 1998 by the Canadian Association of Occupational Therapists (CAOT). Reproduced with permission of CAOT Publication.

Cost-Consequence Analyses

A cost-consequence analysis can be used to portray a health service or to compare two or more health interventions. This type of analysis requires that investigators provide a descriptive profile of the cost of intervention as well as any health and economic outcomes. Intervention costs might include expenditures associated with hospital use and drug consumption, out-of-pocket expenses, and any intangible costs such as caregiver burden. Health outcomes might be assessed in multiple domains such as physical, social, and psychological well being. The primary economic outcomes that might be reported in the evaluation could include alterations in the future employment earnings of service recipients, any positive or negative changes in the personal income or spending of service recipients, and any positive or negative changes in future expenditures on health.

Cost-consequence evaluations simply provide descriptive summaries regarding different costs and outcomes, but they do not total or sum these values. The weighting or relative importance of these variables is left to the user of the evaluation. This type of analysis is based on the premise that users can and should make the value judgment trade-offs necessary to integrate a disparate list of pros and cons. Torrance, Siegel, and Luce (1996) recommended that a cost-consequence analysis form the descriptive basis for other types of economic evaluations when these assessments are used to compare two or more interventions.

Feldman, Latimer, and Davidson (1996) provided an example of a cost-consequence analysis. These investigators conducted an evaluation to described the costs and outcomes associated with the delivery of home care services by way of a cluster care program versus a traditional model of service delivery. They described and compared the costs and consequences (i.e., mortality, functional status, depressive symptoms, and service satisfaction) with persons who received these two models of home-based services.

Cost-Effectiveness Analyses

A cost-effectiveness analysis describes and compares the costs and health outcomes of two or more health services. Economic outcomes are neither measured nor reported. In addition, these evaluations require that services produce the same type of outcome so that the results can be used to compare interventions in terms of their costs per unit of health effect or health effects per unit of cost (Drummond, O'Brien, Stoddart, & Torrance, 1997; Russell, Gold, Siegel, Daniels, & Weinstein, 1996). For example, if the purpose of two different services was to improve the disability status of a specific group of persons, these interventions could be compared in terms of the resources used by each approach to produce the same effect on health (i.e., costs per unit of disability status). Alternatively, the services could be compared in terms of how much they affect health for each dollar spent (i.e., health effect per unit of cost). Refer to Box 1 for a clinical scenario that illustrates this concept.

Cost-effectiveness analyses require that the services being compared produce the same type of outcome or effect on health. For example, it would be appropriate to use this type of evaluation to compare two services that were designed to prevent fall-related injuries in elderly persons who live in the community. Rizzo, Baker, McAvay, and Tinetti (1996) con-

---

Box 1
**Calculating and Comparing the Cost-Effectiveness of
Two Rehabilitation Services**

Consider the following scenario and the contribution of a cost-effectiveness analysis to the decision-making process. Assume that a payer was trying to determine the relative value of two approaches to rehabilitation that were designed to improve the disability status of a defined population. A team of investigators determined that the typical recipient of Service A received 30 hr of care (i.e., valued at $35/hr) and improved their disability status by 150 units. Recipients of Service B received 10 hr of care (i.e., valued at $40/hr) and improved their disability status by 100 units.[2]

The cost-effectiveness of Service A would equal $7 per unit of change in disability status (i.e., $1,050 [30 hr x $35/hr] for 150 units of change; $1,050 ÷ 150 units = $7 per unit). By comparison, the cost-effectiveness of Service B would equal $4 per unit of change in disability status (i.e., $400 [10 hr x $40/hr] for 100 units of change; $400 ÷ 100 units = $4 per unit). Therefore, the cost per unit of change for Service B is superior to Service A.

Alternately, if a payer spent $1,000 for Service A, a typical service recipient could be expected to attain a change in disability status of approximately 143 units (i.e., $1,050/150 units = $1,000/x where x = 143 units). If this same $1,000 was used as payment toward Service B, a change in disability status of approximately 250 units could be expected (i.e., $400/100 units = $1,000/x where x = 250 units). Therefore, the approach to rehabilitation that has the most effect on disability is Service B. In essence, health services can be ranked, and interventions with the lowest cost per unit of outcome (e.g., $4 for Service B) or the highest effect on health per unit of investment (e.g., Service B) are the most efficient ways to improve the health of a defined population (Russell, Siegel, et al., 1996).

---

[2]Assume for the purpose of this example that recipients of both services were initially similar and their outcomes were measured using the same standardized instrument. The assumption regarding case-mix similarities between groups will be discussed in chapter 8 under the heading "Sample Assignment."

---

ducted a cost-effectiveness analysis when they compared the delivery of a new fall prevention program with the delivery of routine care. These investigators calculated the cost-effectiveness of the new approach by calculating the costs per fall prevented (i.e., cost per unit of health effect).

It would not be appropriate to use cost-effectiveness analyses to compare a service that enhanced vocational preparedness with a service that promoted independence in self-care. In this context, it may be more appropriate to use a cost-consequence, cost-utility, or cost-benefit analysis as these approaches to economic evaluation help investigators and decision makers to compare services that affect different domains of health (e.g., vocational preparedness and independence in self-care). Cost-utility and cost-benefit analyses are described in more detail in chapter 5.

The results of a cost-effectiveness analysis can be summarized using a cost-effectiveness ratio (CE ratio). The Panel on Cost-Effectiveness in Health and Medicine, a group convened by the United States Public Health Service, recommended that a CE ratio capture changes in resource use and improvements in health that are associated with an intervention (Weinstein, Siegel, Gold, Kamlet, & Russell, 1996). Torrance et al. (1996) summarized the components of the CE ratio in the following equation:

$$\text{CE Ratio} = \frac{\text{Total Cost (TC) of Specific Service} - \text{TC of Comparison Service}}{\substack{\text{Total Health Outcomes (THO) of Specific Service} \\ - \text{THO of Comparison Service}}}$$

The numerator of a cost-effectiveness ratio is computed by determining the differences in costs between two service alternatives (i.e., net changes in resource use or incremental costs), whereas the denominator is calculated by determining the differences in health outcomes between the services (i.e., net improvements or incremental effectiveness). For example, the scenario described in Box 1 illustrates a situation where investigators are conducting a cost-effectiveness analysis of Service A and B. The typical recipient of Service A received 30 hr of care at $35/hr and improved their disability status by 150 units. Recipients of Service B received 10 hr of care at $40/hr and improved their disability status by 100 units.[3] The cost-effectiveness ratio for Service A or the incremental costs and effects of this intervention is equal to $650/50 units. Therefore, the incremental costs of Service A includes the expenses associated with the additional expenditures on this intervention (i.e., $650), and the incremental outcomes attained by participation in this service (i.e., 50 additional units of functional status).

However, cost-effectiveness analyses are slightly different than most efficiency assessments: the former requires a determination of the cost per unit of a health outcome. By comparison, efficiency measures often evaluate the productivity of the care process. Therefore, most efficiency indicators assess the cost per unit of through-put whereas cost-effectiveness analyses are used to determine the cost per unit of outcome.

---

[3]Assume for the purpose of this example that recipients of both services were initially similar and the outcomes were measured using the same standardized instrument. The assumption regarding case-mix similarities between groups will be discussed in chapter 8 under the heading "Sample Assignment."

Benefits and Challenges

Cost-consequence and cost-effectiveness analyses both offer a structure for identifying, measuring, and valuing service costs and effects and a process by which various services can be compared (Wolff, Helminiak, & Kraemer Tebers, 1997). One of the advantages of using cost-effectiveness analyses is that investigators can provide decision makers with information regarding the relative value of alternative interventions in terms of achieving change in a specific outcome or dimension of health. Cost-consequence analyses can be used to describe and compare programs that affect service recipients in different or multiple domains of health. In addition, economic outcomes can be calculated and reported.

The Office of Technology Assessment (1980) reported that prior to the 1980s there did not appear to be a corresponding increase in the use of cost-consequence and cost-effectiveness analysis for decision-making around the adoption and use of new technology. Stoddart (1982) argued that most of these evaluations took a viewpoint that was different than the perspective of the target audience. It is important when designing an evaluation to consider the perspective of the audience for whom the final report will be written. Chapters 3 and 9 provide more discussion on this topic.

Implicit in all economic evaluations is the notion that finances are limited, as the results of these analyses are intended to aid decision makers in allocating resources among various services and recipients. Evaluations that have been conducted from the perspective of society, payers, or service providers may be at odds with the wishes or best interests of other persons. For example, the results of an evaluation may suggest that the financial resources required to pay for one person to receive an expensive intervention be redirected to pay for services that would do more to improve the health of others. More often than not, the results of these evaluations can be used to identify the health service that would be most efficient in attaining desired health outcomes. Although the results of these evaluations inform decision makers about the relative magnitude of service costs and outcomes, other factors such as equity and fairness need to be considered when making important judgments regarding the allocation of limited resources (Russell, Siegel, et al., 1996).

One potential drawback of conducting economic evaluations is that the findings might not be deemed to be valid by some persons. For example, critics of these evaluative methods contend that it is impossible to place an accurate value on the true costs and outcomes of health programs and that imprecise or erroneous assessments are less useful than not conducting an evaluation. This criticism could also be directed toward clinical and program evaluations. Fuchs (1980) argued that choices must be made and that the only option is whether to evaluate "explicitly, systematically, and openly" using these methods, or to evaluate "implicitly, haphazardly, and secretly, as has been done so often in the past" (p. 937).

Since the early 1990s there has been a movement toward standardizing the methods used to conduct evaluations of health service costs and outcomes. In 1996 the Public Health Service published national guidelines to enhance the quality, rigor, validity, comparability, and the value of cost-effectiveness analyses to decision makers (Gold, Siegel, Russell, & Weinstein, 1996). In addition, the current popularity of the evidence-based practice movement emphasizes the value and importance of basing clinical and administrative decision-making on scientific evidence from research (Evidence-Based Medicine Working Group, 1992; Law & Baum, 1998).

Summary

Economic evaluations should provide decision makers with information regarding the relative value of health services by describing the resource contributions (i.e., costs of a service) and outcomes (i.e., health and economic effects) associated with interventions. Cost-consequence and cost-effectiveness analyses are the most common methods used to determine and demonstrate the value of clinical services. Cost-consequence analyses describe the costs and outcomes of a service and can be used to describe an intervention or compare two or more interventions that affect different or multiple domains of health. In addition, economic outcomes can be calculated and reported. Cost-effectiveness analyses can be used to compare the relative costs and effectiveness of services that produce the same type of outcome. ❖

Practice Exercises

You have been asked to conduct a cost-consequence or cost-effectiveness analysis for an outpatient return-to-work program that is offered 3 hr/day 5 days per week. The evaluation will be used to market this program to different employers and health plans, and you have decided to conduct the analysis from the payer perspective. The target population of the service is persons who have had a recent myocardial infarction.

The program supervisor provided you with information on the average amount billed per client per day and the length of time clients typically receive services. The average length of time each worker spends in the program is 4 weeks, but 75% of clients are discharged after 3 weeks. After holding a discussion with some of the staff members and clientele, you decided to collect information regarding changes in clients' endurance levels, mobility status, and perceptions regarding their ability to return to work. This data will be collected upon admission to the program and after clients have received services for 3 weeks. The program staff members indicated that they believe that workers who participate in the program return to work sooner than they would have if they had not participated in the program. Refer to Appendix D for responses to all exercise questions.

1. Specify the perspective of the analysis.
2. Use the conceptual framework furnished in Figure 2 in chapter 2 to provide a descriptive profile of this health service.
3. What information would investigators provide in an evaluation report if a cost-consequence analysis was conducted?
4. What information would investigators provide in an evaluation report if a cost-effectiveness analysis was conducted? Be sure to identify the comparable service and incorporate a discussion regarding the concept of incremental costs and outcomes.
5. Complete Table 5 to become familiar with how costs and outcomes vary by perspective.

Table 5
A Descriptive Summary of the Costs and Outcomes of a Health Service From Various Perspectives

Perspective	Costs (Resource Contributions)		Outcomes (Service Effects)	
	Financial	Nonfinancial	Health	Economic
Payer				
Health care provider				
Client/consumer/ patient				

References

Drummond, M. F., O'Brien, B. J., Stoddart, G. L., & Torrance, G. (1997). *Methods for the economic evaluation of health care programmes* (2nd ed.). Oxford, UK: Oxford University Press.

Evidence-Based Medicine Working Group. (1992). Evidence-based medicine: A new approach to teaching the practice of medicine. *Journal of the American Medical Association, 268,* 2420–2425.

Feldman, P. H., Latimer, E., & Davidson, H. (1996). Medicaid-funded home care for the frail elderly and disabled: Evaluating the cost savings and outcomes of a service delivery reform. *Health Services Research, 31*, 489–508.

Fuchs, V. R. (1980). What is CBA/CEA, and why are they doing this to us? *New England Journal of Medicine, 303*, 937–938.

Gold, M. R., Siegel, J. E., Russell, L. B., & Weinstein, M. C. (Eds.). (1996). *Cost-effectiveness in health and medicine.* New York: Oxford University Press.

Law, M., & Baum, C. (1998). Evidence-based occupational therapy. *Canadian Journal of Occupational Therapy, 65*, 131–135.

Office of Technology Assessment. (1980). *The implications of cost-effectiveness: Analysis of medical technology.* Washington, DC: Government Printing Office.

Rizzo, J. A., Baker, D. I., McAvay, G., & Tinetti, M. E. (1996). The cost-effectiveness of a multifactorial targeted prevention program for falls among community elderly persons. *Medical Care, 34*, 954–969.

Russell, L. B., Gold, M. R., Siegel, J. E., Daniels, N., & Weinstein, M. C. (1996). The role of cost-effectiveness analysis in health and medicine. *Journal of the American Medical Association, 276*, 1172–1177.

Russell, L. B., Siegel, J. E., Daniels, N., Gold, M. R., Luce, B. R., & Mandelblatt, J. S. (1996). Cost-effectiveness analysis as a guide to resource allocation in health: Roles and limitations. In M. R. Gold, J. E. Siegel, L. B. Russell, & M. C. Weinstein (Eds.), *Cost-effectiveness in health and medicine* (pp. 3–24). New York: Oxford University Press.

Stoddart, G. L. (1982). Economic evaluation methods and health policy. *Evaluation and the Health Professions, 5*, 393–414.

Torrance, G. W., Siegel, J. E., & Luce, B. R. (1996). Framing and designing the cost-effectiveness analysis. In M. R. Gold, J. E. Siegel, L. B. Russel, & M. C. Weinstein (Eds.), *Cost-effectiveness in health and medicine* (pp. 54–81). New York: Oxford University Press.

Watson, D., & Mathews, M. (1998). Economic evaluation of occupational therapy: Where are we at? *Canadian Journal of Occupational Therapy, 65*, 160–167.

Weinstein, M. C., Siegel, J. E., Gold, M. R., Kamlet, M. S., & Russell, L. B. (1996). Recommendations of the Panel on Cost-Effectiveness in Health and Medicine. *Journal of the American Medical Association, 276*, 1253–1258.

White House Domestic Policy Council (1993). *Health security: The President's report to the American people.* Washington, DC: Author.

Wolff, N., Helminiak, T. W., & Kraemer Tebes, J. (1997). Getting the cost right in cost-effectiveness analyses. *American Journal of Psychiatry, 154*, 736–743.

5
Cost-Utility and Cost-Benefit Analyses

Over history and across cultures many people have been highly satisfied with use-less treatment nostrums which are without merit medically or in terms of more objectively conceived quality of life. Mere popular acceptance does not mean that a treatment truly enhances quality of life apart from imagined benefits. (Jenkins, 1992, p. 371)

Learning Objectives
* Define and describe cost-utility and cost-benefit analyses.
* List the benefits and challenges of these two types of evaluation.

Although all of the different types of economic evaluation measure the costs and outcomes associated with the delivery and consumption of a health service, cost-utility and cost-benefit analyses differ primarily in the way they measure outcomes. Cost-effectiveness analyses can be used to describe and compare the relative costs and effectiveness of services that affect the same domain of health. However, many investigators are interested in comparing services that each affect different domains of health. For example, consider a situation where a decision maker must determine whether to offer an educational program to persons who have experienced a recent stroke or a support program for spouses of persons who have severe neuromuscular disorders. It is expected that these interventions would have an effect on different domains of health if the educational program was designed to enhance the level of knowledge among stroke survivors and the support program was structured to promote the development of coping skills among spouses. In this context a cost-effectiveness analysis would not help investigators to adequately compare the relative value of these two services as these interventions do not affect the same domain of health. One program has been designed to enhance knowledge, whereas the other intervention addresses the coping skills of service recipients.

There are three different types of evaluation that help investigators to compare services that affect different domains of health: (a) cost-utility, (b) cost-benefit, and (c) cost-consequence analyses. Cost-utility and cost-benefit analyses can be used to compare interventions that affect different domains of health, as these methods require that investigators employ the same unit of measurement when assessing the outcomes of each service. Cost-utility analyses require that the outcomes of each intervention be measured in terms of health status or the value of that status to the client or both. By comparison, cost-benefit analyses require that the outcomes of each intervention be measured in monetary values. A summary of these two approaches to evaluation is provided in Table 6.

Despite the advantages of cost-utility and cost-benefit analyses in providing information to decision makers regarding the relative value of two or more services, there are circumstances when these approaches to economic evaluation may not be appropriate. In these situations, it may be more feasible to conduct a cost-consequence analysis, which can be used to provide a descriptive comparison of two or more interventions that affect different or multiple domains of health. In addition, economic outcomes can also be calculated and reported with this type of analysis. Cost-consequence analyses are described in more detail in chapter 4.

Selecting the most appropriate type of economic evaluation to use requires that investigators identify the most relevant outcomes to include in the assessment. This determination is made after consideration is given to the objectives of the service, the perspective and scope of the evaluation, and the information needs of the audience for whom the evaluation is targeted. A more thorough discussion on this topic is provided in chapter 3.

Cost-Utility Analyses

As outlined in chapter 2, rehabilitation programs can have an effect on the health and economic status of people. Cost-utility analyses require that investigators evaluate health outcomes in terms of changes in health-related quality of life or the quality and quantity of life that accrues to service recipients who participate in particular health service programs. The results of these evaluations can be used to compare services in terms of their costs per unit of change in health status. These analyses do not evaluate the economic effect of interventions but assume that this outcome influences how service recipients rate their quality of life. Health-related quality of life is a subjective, multidimensional concept that describes a person's functional abilities and his or her preference for a particular health state (Laplege & Hunt, 1997; Oldridge et al., 1993). As all inter-

Table 6
Summary of Measures and Results of Cost-Utility and Cost-Benefit Analyses

Type of Evaluation	Measurement Unit		Presentation of Results	Example Evaluation
	Cost of Service	Consequences		
Cost-utility	Total intervention costs including start-up and ongoing expenditures	Health status Healthy years QALY	Cost per change in health status Cost per healthy year Cost per QALY	Rissanen et al. (1997) conducted a cost-utility analysis when they calculated the cost and change in quality of life among persons who received a total knee or total hip replacement.
Cost-benefit	Total intervention costs including start-up and ongoing expenditures	Total financial outcome derived from determining the monetary value of both health and economic outcomes	Ratio of cost of service to cost of consequence(s) Net cost or net benefit	Gold, Gafni, Nelligan, and Millson (1997) conducted cost-benefit analysis to determine the net financial effect of offering a needle exchange program to prevent HIV transmission among persons who share injection needles.

Note. QALY = quality adjusted life year. Adapted from "Economic Evaluation of Occupational Therapy: Where Are We At?" by D. E. Watson & M. Mathews, 1998. *Canadian Journal of Occupational Therapy, 65,* p.162. Copyright 1998 by the Canadian Association of Occupational Therapists (CAOT). Reproduced with permission of CAOT Publications.

ventions are ultimately provided to affect health-related quality of life, it would follow that health services could be compared on this basis.

Investigators who conduct cost-utility analyses use a variety of scales to measure health-related quality of life. Some of the more popular scales include the Medical Outcomes Study 36-item Short-Form Health Survey (SF-36) (Ware & Sherbourne, 1992), the Rosser Disability Distress Scale

(RDDS) (Rosser & Kind, 1978), the Quality of Well-Being Questionnaire (Kaplan & Bush, 1976), the European Quality of Life Measure (EURQUOL Group, 1990) and the Health Measurement Questionnaire (Kind & Gudex, 1994). Appendix A provides a summary of instruments that have been used to evaluate different rehabilitation services based on their effect on quality of life.

Investigators who specialize in conducting cost-utility analyses have occasionally used *utility values* to measure quality of life and the value of that health status to the patient (Guyatt, 1995; Weinstein & Stason, 1977). Utility values are calculated using a health status index that essentially serves as a weighting scheme; all definable health states from death to full health are assigned a weight, or utility, from 0 to 1. These values can be obtained using judgment, the literature, or measurements derived from a sample of participants (Drummond, O'Brien, Stoddart, & Torrance, 1997). Utility values that are derived from judgment rely on clinicians or investigators to assess the relative worth of different health states. Alternatively, utility values can be borrowed from analyses published in the literature. Both of these approaches were used by Goel, Deber, and Detsky (1989) when they evaluated the outcomes of using radiographic media. Investigators can measure the preferences that a sample of participants who are affected by the intervention have toward various health states by using the standard gamble or time trade-off approach. Evaluations that incorporate the standard gamble approach ask persons what risks they would incur to achieve a given health outcome. The time trade-off approach requires that persons identify the number of years of life they would exchange in return for a given health status. Drummond et al. (1997) provided a detailed description of these methods.

Quality-adjusted life years (QALY) is another measurement construct that has been used by investigators to assess the effects of services on the quantity and health-related quality of life (Guyatt, 1995; Weinstein & Stason, 1977). QALY are calculated by multiplying a utility score by the length of time spent at a given health status to yield a figure equivalent to the number of years with full health (Weinstein & Stason, 1977). Oldridge et al. (1993) conducted a cost-utility analysis of a cardiac rehabilitation program and calculated the cost per QALY for persons who experienced an acute myocardial infarction and received this intervention.

Investigators who conduct cost-utility analyses using QALY to measure outcomes assess changes in both the quantity and health-related quality of life. As some decision makers may deem these measurement strategies as unethical (Fuchs, 1980; Phelps & Mushlin, 1991), it may be more appropriate to use instruments that simply measure health-related quality of life but do not incorporate changes in the quantity of life (Drummond et al., 1997). McCulloch (1991) provided an overview regarding the use of health status measures and QALY to assess the health outcomes of rehabilitation services.

Cost-utility analyses may not be appropriate to use when intermediate outcomes are more appropriate to assess. For example, when a service has been designed to affect health at the impairment or disability level, instruments that measure change in quality of life may not capture clinically significant improvements in biological or functional health. In addition, it could be argued that health care practitioners primarily target interventions toward specific medical and rehabilitation needs of clients. In this context, these health care practitioners should not be expected to be held accountable for the overall health-related quality of life of service recipients as they do not have direct control over other important determinants of health (e.g., social, economic, environmental).

Rissanen et al. (1997) provided an example of a cost-utility analysis. These investigators conducted an evaluation to calculate the cost of medical and rehabilitation intervention and measured changes in the quality of life among persons who receive a total hip or total knee replacement. A cost-effectiveness analysis was also conducted when Rissanen et al. (1997) compared the costs and effectiveness of each of these surgeries on the health status of persons of different age groups. These researchers determined that the cost per unit of change in health was lowest among younger patients rather than older patients. In addition, there was more variation in the cost-effectiveness of joint replacements among patients who received a knee replacement than those who received a hip. Health status was measured using a 15-dimension measure of health-related quality of life, whereas disability status was measured using a 14-item scale of activities of daily living.

Cost-Benefit Analyses

As outlined in chapter 2, rehabilitation programs can have an effect on the health and economic status of people. Cost-benefit analyses require that both of these outcomes be measured in monetary values and that these financial figures be compared with the cost of providing the intervention. The results of this type of analysis can be presented in terms of a ratio (e.g., financial costs to financial outcomes) or as a sum of costs and benefits (i.e., net financial effect). When the value of the sum of costs and outcomes is negative, costs are greater than benefits (i.e., net costs); when this quotient is positive, benefits are greater than costs (i.e., net benefits) (Zarnke, Levine, & O'Brien, 1997). By valuing the health and economic outcomes of a service in money terms so as to make them commensurate with the valuation of costs, it is possible to ascertain whether financial outcomes justify the investment (Weinstein & Stason, 1977).

As it is difficult to measure health outcomes in monetary terms, investigators who specialize in conducting cost-benefit analyses have employed estimates of willingness-to-pay or willingness-to-accept to translate these outcomes into monetary figures (Diener, O'Brien, & Gafni,

1997; O'Brien & Gafni, 1996; O'Brien & Viramontes, 1994). Willingness-to-pay has been proposed as a measure to quantify a person's willingness to pay for participation in a program, whereas willingness-to-accept could be used to measure the minimum a person would need to be compensated to forego involvement in a program (O'Brien & Viramontes, 1994). These estimates could then be used to calculate the monetary value of different health outcomes to persons who receive a service.

The primary economic outcomes that occur as a result of (i.e., after) participation in a service include alterations in the future employment earnings of service recipients, any positive or negative changes in the personal income or spending of service recipients, and any positive or negative changes in future expenditures on health. Therefore, cost-benefit analyses are particularly useful when one of the primary objectives of a health service is to prevent future service use or when the target audience is primarily interested in the net financial effect of rendering a service. The following three studies provide examples of the use of cost-benefit analyses for these purposes.

Rizzo, Baker, McAvay, and Tinetti (1996) conducted a cost-benefit evaluation of an intervention program that was designed to reduce the frequency of falls among high-risk, elderly persons who lived in the community. The comparison group included seniors who did not receive this service. Although the prevention of falls may have implications for the health of service recipients, the primary objective of the intervention program was to prevent future service use. The intervention costs (i.e., fall prevention program) were calculated and compared with the financial savings that would accrue from reductions in expenditures on hospital, nursing home, and home health services (i.e., economic outcomes). The target audience of the evaluation was persons who had vested interests in the net financial effect of offering the intervention. The analysis was conducted from the perspective of both service delivery providers and payers.

Ruchlin and Morris (1981) conducted a cost-benefit analysis to determine the value of providing an emergency alarm and response system to seniors to help them to safely maintain their independence at home. The comparison group included seniors who did not receive this service. These investigators calculated the intervention costs (i.e., emergency alarm and response system) and compared this with the savings that would accrue from reductions in the expenditures on institutional care, formal community services, and informal support services (i.e., economic outcomes). This analysis helped the investigators to calculate the net financial effect of offering this service. The analysis was conducted from the societal perspective.

Margolis and Petti (1994) conducted a cost-benefit analysis to determine the value of offering a new service in a community. These investigators estimated the potential financial effect of offering home-based, family-centered services to children with psychiatric disorders who would otherwise receive services in a psychiatric hospital. The intervention costs (i.e., care in the community) were calculated and compared with the savings that would accrue from reductions in expenditures on hospital services (i.e., economic outcome). This analysis helped these investigators to determine the net financial effect of offering community-based care to this clientele. The analysis was conducted from the payer perspective.

Summary

Cost-utility analyses require that costs be related to the effect of an intervention where health outcomes are measured in terms of changes in the quantity and health-related quality of life. The results of these evaluations can be used to compare services in terms of their costs per unit of change in health status. In practice, these evaluations are most appropriate when the primary objective of a program is to affect the quality of life of service recipients. By comparison, cost-benefit analyses require that intervention costs be compared with the monetary value of health and economic outcomes to determine whether the effect of the service was worth the investment. In practice, these evaluations are particularly useful when the primary objective of a health service is to prevent future service use and the target audience of the evaluation report is interested in the net financial effect of a service.

The ultimate goal of investigators who conduct economic evaluations is to provide decision makers with information regarding the relative value of a health service. Although all of these evaluations measure the costs and outcomes associated with the delivery and consumption of a health service, cost-utility and cost-benefit analyses help decision makers to compare programs and interventions that affect different or multiple domains. This is achieved by having investigators employ the same unit of measurement when assessing the outcomes of services that are being compared. ❖

Practice Exercises

You have decided to conduct a cost-benefit analysis on the provision of Level II fieldwork to occupational therapy students. As the results of the evaluation will be used to recruit and retain fieldwork sites, it will be important to provide health care organizations with relevant information regarding the relative value of offering these educational experiences. To begin the assessment, a review of the literature was conducted. This review was undertaken to determine whether this type of study had been conducted before and the relevance of the methods, findings, and conclusions used in other studies to the current assessment. You have only found an article by Shalik (1987)[4] that was published more than 10 years ago, and

---

[4]Refer to Shalik (1987) for a discussion regarding the determination of costs and benefits from the perspective of a fee-for-service organization and to Kirz and Larsen (1986) for a discussion regarding the determination of costs and benefits from the viewpoint of a prepaid, managed care organization.

you have decided to replicate a similar study. To prepare the purpose statement or research question for your evaluation, provide responses to the following questions. Answers are provided in Appendix D.

1. Describe the service that will be evaluated.
2. What is the comparison service?
3. What will be the perspective of the analysis?
4. Identify the most relevant and important costs to include in the analysis.
5. How might these costs be measured and valued?
6. What outcomes should be included in the analysis?
7. How might these outcomes be measured and valued?
8. Write a statement of purpose or research question for your evaluation.

References

Diener, A., O'Brien, B., & Gafni, A. (1997). *Health care contingent valuation studies: A review and classification of the literature (Working Paper 07-06).* Hamilton, Ontario: Centre for Health Economics and Policy Analysis.

Drummond, M. F., O'Brien, B. J., Stoddart, G. L., & Torrance, G. (1997). *Methods for the economic evaluation of health care programmes* (2nd ed.). Oxford, UK: Oxford University Press.

EUROQUOL Group. (1990). A new facility for the measurement of health related quality of life. *Health Policy, 16,* 435–441.

Fuchs, V. R. (1980). What is CBA/CEA, and why are they doing this to us? *New England Journal of Medicine, 303,* 937–938.

Goel, V., Deber, R. D., & Detsky, A. S. (1989). Non-ionic contrast media: Economic analysis and health policy development. *Canadian Medical Association Journal, 150,* 389–395.

Gold, M., Gafni, A., Nelligan, P., & Millson, P. (1997). Needle exchange programs: An economic evaluation of a local experience. *Canadian Medical Association Journal, 157,* 25–262.

Guyatt, G. (1995). A taxonomy of health status instruments. *Journal of Rheumatology, 22,* 1188–1190.

Jenkins, C. D. (1992). Social science and medicine. *Assessment of outcomes of health intervention* (pp. 367–375). Elsevier Science.

Kaplan, R. M., & Bush, J. W. (1976). Health status: Types of validity and the index of well-being. *Health Services Research,* 478–507.

Kind, P., & Gudex, C. M. (1994). Measuring health status in the community: A comparison of methods. *Journal of Epidemiology and Community Health, 48,* 86–91.

Kirz, H. L., & Larsen, C. (1986). Costs and benefits of medical student training to a health maintenance organization. *Journal of the American Medical Association, 256,* 734–739.

Laplege, A., & Hunt, S. (1997). The problem of quality of life in medicine. *Journal of the American Medical Association, 278,* 47–50.

Margolis, L. H., & Petti, R. D. (1994). An analysis of the costs and benefits of two strategies to decrease length in children's psychiatric hospitals. *Health Services Research, 29,* 155–167.

McCulloch, D. (1991). Can we measure "output?" Quality-adjusted life years, health indices and occupational therapy. *British Journal of Occupational Therapy, 54,* 219–221.

O'Brien, B., & Gafni, A. (1996). When do the "dollars" make sense? Toward a conceptual framework for contingent valuation studies in health care. *Medical Decision Making, 16,* 288–299.

O'Brien, B., & Viramontes, J. L. (1994). Willingness to pay: A valid and reliable measure of health state preference? *Medical Decision Making, 14,* 289–297.

Oldridge, N., Furlong, W., Feeny, D., Torrance, G., Guyatt, G., Crowe, J., & Jones, N. (1993). Economic evaluation of cardiac rehabilitation soon after myocardial infarction. *American Journal of Cardiology, 72,* 154–161.

Phelps, C. E., & Mushlin, A. I. (1991). On the (near) equivalence of cost-effectiveness and cost-benefit analyses. *International Journal of Technology Assessment in Health Care, 7,* 12–21.

Rissanen, P., Aro, P., Sintonen, H., Asikainen, K., Slätis, P., & Paavolainen, P. (1997). Costs and cost-effectiveness in hip and knee replacements: A prospective study. *International Journal of Technology Assessment in Health Care, 13,* 575–588.

Rizzo, J. A., Baker, D. I., McAvay, G., & Tinetti, M. E. (1996). The cost-effectiveness of a multifactorial targeted prevention program for falls among community elderly persons. Medical Care, *34,* 954–969.

Rosser, R., & Kind, P. (1978). A scale of valuation of states of illness: Is there a social consensus? *International Journal of Epidemiology,* 478–507.

Ruchlin, H. S., & Morris, J. N. (1981). Cost-benefit analysis of an emergency alarm and response system: A case study of a long-term care program. *Health Services Research, 16,* 65–80.

Shalik, L. D. (1987). Cost-benefit analysis of Level II fieldwork in occupational therapy. *American Journal of Occupational Therapy, 41,* 638–645.

Ware, J. E., & Sherbourne, C. (1992). The Medical Outcomes Study 36-item Short-Form Health Survey (SF-36). *Medical Care, 30,* 473–481.

Watson, D. E., & Mathews, M. (1998). Economic evaluation of occupational therapy: Where are we at? *Canadian Journal of Occupational Therapy, 65,* 160–167

Weinstein, M. C., & Stason, W. B. (1977). Foundations of cost-effectiveness analysis for health and medical practices. *New England Journal Medicine, 296,* 716–721.

Zarnke, K. B., Levine, M. A., & O'Brien, B. J. (1997). Cost benefit analyses in the health-care literature: Don't judge a study by its label. *Journal of Clinical Epidemiology, 50,* 813–822.

Learning Resources

Cost-Utility Analyses

Diener, A., O'Brien, B., & Gafni, A. (1997). *Health care contingent valuation studies: A review and classification of the literature (Working Paper 07-06).* Hamilton, Ontario, Canada: Centre for Health Economics and Policy Analysis.

McCulloch, D. (1991). Can we measure "output?" Quality-adjusted life years, health indices and occupational therapy. *British Journal of Occupational Therapy, 54,* 219–221.

O'Brien, B., & Gafni, A. (1996). When do the "dollars" make sense? Toward a conceptual framework for contingent valuation studies in health care. *Medical Decision Making, 16,* 288–299.

O'Brien, B., & Viramontes, J. L. (1994). Willingness to pay: A valid and reliable measure of health state preference? *Medical Decision Making, 14,* 289–297.

Rittenhouse, B. E. (1997). Healthy years equivalents versus time trade-off: Ambiguity on certainty and uncertainty. *International Journal of Technology Assessment in Health Care, 13,* 1, 35–48.

Torrance, G. W. (1986). Measurement of health state utilities for economic appraisal: A review. *Journal of Health Economics, 5,* 1–30.

Cost-Benefit Analyses

Fuchs, V. R. (1980). What is CBA/CEA, and why are they doing this to us? *New England Journal of Medicine, 303,* 16, 937–938.

Zarnke, K. B., Levine, M. A., & O'Brien, B. J. (1997). Cost-benefit analyses in the health-care literature: Don't judge a study by its label. *Journal of Clinical Epidemiology, 50,* 813–822.

6

Identifying and Measuring the Outcomes of Clinical Services

The fundamental problem in America is not that we spend too little for health care. It is that we don't get good value for the billions of dollars we spend. (White House Domestic Policy Council, 1993, p. 10)

Learning Objectives

- Describe the steps to take when identifying the health and economic outcomes of a clinical service.
- Identify and describe a conceptual model of outcomes.
- List some of the issues to consider when selecting relevant outcomes.
- Define the different psychometric properties that are important to consider when selecting an instrument to measure outcomes.
- List and define the different types of validity and reliability.

Health interventions vary in the effect they have on service recipients, and persons differ in the importance they attribute toward various outcomes. Therefore, investigators who conduct economic evaluations try to determine the clinical effectiveness of health interventions in attaining specific outcomes for "typical" service recipients. *Clinical effectiveness* refers to the type and level of benefit that could be expected when "average" practitioners provide a health service to "typical" service recipients under ordinary circumstances. Effectiveness research is different from efficacy studies as the latter are conducted to determine the level of benefit that could be expected when interventions are provided by the most skilled practitioners under ideal or well-controlled conditions (Lohr, 1988; Office of Technology Assessment, 1978). The clinical effectiveness of an intervention should be established before any assessment of costs, as it would be inappropriate and wasteful to calculate the cost of providing ineffective services (Drummond, O'Brien, Stoddart, & Torrance, 1997).

The most challenging steps to take when conducting a clinical evaluation include identifying the most relevant and important health and economic outcomes, selecting appropriate methods to measure these intended benefits, and attributing these outcomes to participation in a specific health service. However, the information compiled through this process can be used to provide evidence regarding the effectiveness of an intervention and combined with costing information to demonstrate the value of a service.

There are basically two steps to follow when assessing the effect of a clinical service. Step 1 involves identifying the most relevant and important health and economic outcomes to include in the evaluation. Consideration should be given to the goals, objectives, and activities of the health service; the needs of the target population and service recipients; and the perspective of the analysis. This process helps investigators to select outcomes that are mutually important to all stakeholders. The first section of this chapter provides information on how to identify relevant outcomes. A number of conceptual frameworks are described to assist investigators in this process.

Step 2 requires that investigators collect evidence regarding the type and level of effect that an intervention has on service recipients. When investigators are conducting an evaluation to assist decision makers in determining whether to offer a new service, evidence from the literature can be collected to determine the effectiveness of an intervention. Cost estimates can then be calculated and combined with this information to help make judgments regarding the value of an intervention. When investigators are conducting an evaluation of a service that is currently offered they must review the literature, identify and measure outcomes, and attribute these outcomes to the involvement of service recipients in the program. This information can then be combined with cost estimates to calculate the value of a clinical service. As both of these instances required that investigators survey the literature, the second section of this chapter provides information on how to conduct a systematic review and appraisal of the literature.

The purpose of this chapter is to assist investigators in enhancing their knowledge and skill at identifying relevant outcomes that are valued by all stakeholders, appraising evidence from the literature on the effectiveness of a clinical intervention, and selecting psychometrically sound instruments to measure specific outcomes. Some of the important issues regarding the selection and measurement of rehabilitation outcomes will be highlighted. The design and implementation of a rigorous, clinical evaluation to attribute outcomes to the receipt of a specific intervention is a complex process and beyond the scope of this text. However, this topic is addressed in some detail in chapter 8.

Step 1: Identifying the Most Relevant and Important Outcomes

Selecting Outcomes That Are Valued by All Stakeholders

The most relevant and important outcomes to include in an evaluation are those that are valued by all stakeholders. Consideration should be given to identifying the goals, objectives, and activities of a health service; the needs of the target population and service recipients; and the perspective of the analysis. The process of selecting relevant outcomes to assess the effectiveness of a specific service is similar to the process of specifying independent and dependent variables in experimental research. In the context of an evaluation, the independent variable represents the characteristics of the health service, whereas the dependent variable denotes the most important health and economic domains in which the service has an effect. In fact, the costs associated with service delivery could also be considered a dependent variable. Once the health and economic outcomes have been identified, investigators can begin to design a research question that will focus the scope of the evaluation. A discussion regarding the phraseology of a good research question is provided in chapter 3.

The goals, objectives, and activities of a health service should be ascertained, as they provide insight into the type of effect on service recipients that service providers intend to have when they render an intervention. By interviewing clinical and administrative staff members, investigators should identify the target population for whom the service was designed; the characteristics of persons who use the service; the type of service rendered; the intensity, frequency, and duration of the program; and the outcomes that service providers and administrators want to assume responsibility for achieving. This information can be used by investigators to understand the intervention (i.e., independent variable) and define potential outcome indicators (i.e., dependent variables).

Occasionally, clinical and administrative staff members in health service organizations have difficulty distinguishing between process and outcome objectives. For example, when asked the question "What is the objective of this program?" some might respond with statements such as "to provide client-centered care" or "to improve the health of our patients." The delivery of "client-centered care," is a process or implementation objective as it defines how services will be rendered and describes the means by which outcomes will be achieved. Recall from chapter 2 that the process of care represents the technical and humanistic profiles of caregivers or the actions, activities, and procedures that occur between service providers and patients (Donabedian, 1980). By comparison, outcome objectives describe the changes that the program hopes to achieve or the ends toward which the program is working (Rush & Ogborne, 1991). Whereas the statement "to improve the health of our patients" is an outcome objective, many service providers do not want to nor should they be held responsible for the overall health of persons in their care. For example, health care providers target interventions toward the specific needs of a clientele and cannot be expected to have a direct influence on other important determinants of health (e.g., social, economic, environmental). Therefore, it may take time and effort to work with clinical and administrative staff members to identify outcome objectives that could be used in the evaluation. Box 2 provides some questions that may facilitate a discussion with these persons. Rush and Ogborne (1991) wrote an excellent article that provides information to assist investigators in working with clinical and administrative staff members to identify and distinguish between implementation and outcome objectives.

Investigators should also conduct interviews with a sample of service recipients and persons in the population for whom the service is intended to determine the outcomes that are valued by these persons. Investigators who acquire this information and incorporate it into the decision-making process regarding the selection of outcomes ensure that these indicators address and are sensitive to the needs of consumers. Occasionally, there may be discrepancies between the characteristics of persons for whom a service was targeted and those who actually receive the intervention. Chapter 3 provides a discussion regarding this issue. Ultimately, outcome information must be collected from a sample of persons who receive the service.

Another important issue that should be considered when selecting outcomes is the perspective of the analysis; evaluations that are conducted from the same viewpoint as the audience for which they are intended are more likely to be useful (Stoddart, 1982). Economic evaluations can be conducted

---

Box 2
Selecting Outcome Indicators With Service Providers: Probe Questions

What are the primary deliverables of the program?

What health or economic outcomes are within in the scope of control of the program?

For what outcomes should the program be held accountable?

Do the outcomes occur with enough frequency to warrant inclusion in the evaluation?

What outcomes information is easy to collect, analyze, and summarize?

What information can be collected, analyzed, and summarized at a reasonable cost?

from the vantage point of society, the health sector, or consumers; and the perspective employed in the analysis plays a crucial role in determining relevant outcome indicators. For example, an evaluation that is conducted from the viewpoint of an acute care service provider might include the following outcomes in an assessment of cardiac rehabilitation: 30-day mortality and readmission rates. If the evaluation was conducted from the perspective of consumers, the most relevant outcomes might include 1-year mortality, employability, and health-related quality of life.

In theory, the goals, objectives, and activities of a health service should be congruent with the needs of the target population and service recipients. In practice, this does not always occur. Box 3 provides an example of a clinical scenario where this type of discrepancy occurred. The situation becomes more complicated when the outcomes selected by service providers and consumers are not in accordance with those identified the audience for whom the evaluation is being conducted. Ultimately, final decisions regarding the relevance or importance of different outcomes should be made in collaboration with all stakeholders. It is important to remember that there is no "correct" decision. Outcomes that are included in an evaluation may eventually be selected based on the availability of

---

Box 3
Assessing Congruence Among Service Goals, Objectives, and Activities

The goal statement of a health service that offers weekly group therapy to adult women who have fibromyalgia is to enhance the functional and mobility status of these persons. Group sessions span 8 weeks and primarily include educational activities regarding nutrition, lifestyle management, and energy conservation.

Whereas the goal statements of this service focuses on behavior change in the domain of functional and mobility status, the group activities focus on enhancing the level of knowledge of group participants. During recent interviews with service recipients, it was determined that these persons had hopes that group therapy would increase their level of knowledge about fibromyalgia and improve their functional status. In this instance, it would appear the stated goals of the group are not entirely consistent with the priorities of the target population as they do not acknowledge the desire of recipients to attain higher levels of disease-specific knowledge. In addition, the program activities are not entirely consistent with either the goal statement of the program or the priorities of the target population. The activities included in group sessions do not provide the opportunity for service recipients to practice applying new knowledge to enhance their functional or mobility status.

In this situation, investigators must make a decision in collaboration with service providers and recipients as to whether to include disease-specific knowledge and behavior change in the service evaluation.

high-quality data. In addition, all outcome indicators, like any measure, vary in their validity, reliability, sensibility, and responsiveness. These issues will be discussed in the next section of this chapter.

There are a number of different methods by which information can be compiled to identify the most relevant and important outcomes to include in an evaluation. The strategies used by investigators may be formal or informal; and traditional data collection methods such as literature reviews, interviews, focus groups, and questionnaires may be useful. For example, Meyers (1995) hosted individual and focus group interviews with stakeholders and collected information through observation and a document review to identify the costs and outcomes of fieldwork education as perceived by students, site supervisors, administrators, and patients. Qualitative research methods were used to collect and analyze the data compiled through this process. Kirz and Larsen (1986) identified the costs and outcomes of a medical student training program by performing a review of the literature and systematically surveying all stakeholders. These investigators conducted 111 telephone interviews and solicited responses using 14 probe questions. The validity of the results obtained using these approaches were validated using external data sources. For example, the perceptions that service providers had regarding changes in workplace productivity were validated using visit logs.

Conceptual Frameworks

Investigators can use conceptual frameworks to guide their discussions with stakeholders regarding the selection of relevant outcomes. Although there has been little work done to guide the conceptualization of outcomes (Keith, 1995), there are a number of taxonomies that could assist evaluators in identifying these variables. Stoddart (1982) identified three broad categories of health service outcomes that can be used when conducting economic evaluations. This approach to categorizing outcomes most closely reflects the conceptual framework as presented in Figure 2 in chapter 2. *Therapeutic effects* (e.g., changes in physical, social, or emotional functioning) that can be attributed to the service should be considered. *Changes in the quality of life* of service recipients might be included in an evaluation as this factor considers the value that patients attribute toward therapeutic outcomes. Health programs may result in *economic outcomes* such as any positive or negative changes in the productivity or personal income of service recipients. In addition, any alteration in future health service use could be considered an economic outcome—especially if the analysis is conducted from the payer perspective.

Lohr (1988) offered a taxonomy of five health outcomes: (a) death, (b) disease, (c) disability, (d) discomfort, and (e) dissatisfaction. Unexpected, premature, untimely, or avoidable death can be used as an outcome indicator. Langhorne, Wagenaar, and Partridge (1996) used this outcome when they assessed whether stroke survivors who received intensive physical therapy experienced lower fatality rates than persons who received more routine levels of rehabilitation. The effect of this intervention on the rate of mortality was not significant. The use of mortality rates as a rehabilitation outcome is controversial as death is a relatively rare event, and this outcome is often not within the scope of control of rehabilitation practitioners. Mortality rates may be more appropriately incorporated into evaluations of surgical interventions that are conducted to reduce the risk of death (e.g., coronary artery bypass surgery).

The other outcome categories defined by Lohr (1988) may be more applicable to most rehabilitation settings. *Disease* indicators may be pertinent when an intervention alters the progression of a disease or changes the physiological status of service recipients. For example, it may be appropriate to include this type of outcome when evaluating services offered by hand therapy or burn care programs. *Disability* or functional status is the most common outcome used in rehabilitation and in the economic evaluation literature. The level of *discomfort* experienced is often assessed by counting adverse events such as pressure sores, episodes of wandering, aggressive or agitated behaviors, physical assaults, aspirations, suicide attempts, falls, readmissions, preventable complications, or hospitalization. The level of *dissatisfaction* experience by persons who are involved in a health service may be appropriate to measure. For example, Feldman, Latimer, and Davidson (1996) assessed the level of satisfaction and dissatisfaction among service recipients when they conducted a cost-consequence analysis of a new model of home health care.

The World Health Organization's (WHO) taxonomy of impairments, disabilities, and handicaps provides an alternative classification scheme that could be used to assist in the identification of relevant health outcomes. An *impairment* is a loss, abnormality, or disturbance of an anatomical, physiological, mental, or emotional structure or function that may be temporary or permanent (Nagi, 1991; WHO, 1980). Conceptually, impairment outcomes are similar to the disease indicators described in the preceding paragraph. *Disability* refers to "any restriction or lack (resulting from an impairment) of ability to perform an activity in the manner or within the range considered normal" (Nagi, 1991; WHO, 1980, p. 143). Disabilities may be temporary or permanent, reversible or irreversible, progressive or regressive and are "characterized by excesses or deficiencies of customarily expected activity performance and behavior" (WHO, 1980, p. 143). *Handicaps* represent a disadvantage experienced by a person as a result of an impairment or disability "that limit or prevent fulfillment of a role that is normal (depending on age, sex, and social and cultural factors) for that individual" (WHO, 1980, p. 183).[5]

---

[5]From *International Classification of Impairments, Disabilities, and Handicaps*, by the World Health Organization, 1980, pp. 143, 183. Reproduced with permission.

Keith (1995) identified other rehabilitation outcomes: the discharge destination of service recipients, resumption of productive activity that has economic consequences or contributes to community and family life, and the amount and type of assistance provided by others. Kramer (1997) argued that rehabilitation professionals should focus their attention on patient-centered outcome dimensions including recovery of daily living, social, and recreational activities as well as integration into previous environments and satisfaction with care. Whiteneck (1994) commented that the perceived health and functional status of service recipients are legitimate rehabilitation outcomes as these perceptions may be more relevant or important than objective measures of impairment, disability, and handicap.

Important Issues

Complex treatments routinely produce short-, medium-, and long-range outcomes, as well as intended and unintended effects (Torrance, Siegel, & Luce, 1996). The following factors should be considered when selecting and measuring outcomes: timing issues, context, frequency of occurrence, scope of control, data quality, feasibility, and popularity.

Although most providers collect information from service recipients upon admission and discharge from treatment, the time frame within which outcomes are measured should be appropriate to the interventions being evaluated. Admission and discharge data collection periods may be appropriate to use when evaluating interventions that are directed at acute conditions that can be altered or cured by the time the service is terminated. However, the timing of measures that are used to evaluate interventions rendered to persons who have chronic or recurring diseases should be different (Forer, 1996; Keith, 1995). It may also be appropriate to consider the time interval since a disease onset when selecting measures or analyzing data. For example, the outcomes selected for an acute stroke rehabilitation program may be quite different from those chosen for a service that is directed toward stroke survivors who are in later stages of recovery.

Although follow-up periods of 6 to 12 months are commonly reported in the literature, these may not be sufficient to capture medium- and long-range outcomes. Outcomes may occur throughout the lifetime of a person, but these events and situations may be difficult if not possible to measure and attribute toward the receipt of a specific health intervention. The longer the period of time between receipt of a service and the measurement of an outcome, the harder it is to attribute this event toward the consumption of a specific health service. The period of time required to capture time-dependent variables should be appropriate for both the intervention and the population studied and allow sufficient time to accommodate the natural progression of the disease or condition.

Many rehabilitation services attempt to assist clients in maximizing their independent performance of a task within a specific context. As the environmental context has a direct influence on a person's level of independence (Watson, 1997), the measurement of an outcome should logically occur in the target context. For example, services that are rendered to inpatients to help them be independent at home should logically be evaluated by assessing the functional performance of a sample of these persons after discharge.

When the functional status of service recipients is assessed repeatedly to detect clinically and statistically significant changes in performance, it is important that these assessments occur within the same environmental setting. For example, if practitioners evaluated the functional status of service recipients upon admission and again before discharge from an institutional setting, these results may not be comparable to scores obtained when the same assessment is conducted in a home setting.[6]

Outcomes that occur infrequently (e.g., pressure sores) can be used to monitor care, but investigators who want to use statistical techniques to test hypotheses regarding the effectiveness of a clinical intervention at reducing the occurrence of infrequent events will require a large sample of participants. Alternatively, if an outcome event occurs with high frequency, then a smaller number of participants are needed (Orkin, Cohen & Duncan, 1993). Therefore, before an outcome indicator such as an adverse event is selected for inclusion in an evaluation, investigators should determine the frequency with which these incidents occur. Investigators who plan on using multivariate analyses to test hypotheses regarding the significance of participating in a service on the occurrence of dichotomous, adverse outcomes (e.g., aspiration, fall, suicide) should ensure that someone on the research team understands logistic regression.

Whiteneck (1994) commented that investigators tend to focus on measuring changes in the functional performance of service recipients, but the quality and comprehensiveness of rehabilitation plays an important role in determining the level of disability in these persons. He argued that the reason for this focus on disability outcomes is that this construct is more within the scope of control of rehabilitation practitioners. However, the level of handicap or health-related quality of life of service recipients is strongly influenced by other factors and determinants of health that may be beyond the scope of control of rehabilitation practitioners. Therefore, before an outcome indicator such as health-related quality of life or mortality rates is selected, investigators should consider how much these outcomes are within the scope of control of rehabilitation service providers.

Forer (1996) recommended that investigators consider the source of data and how this influences the completeness and accuracy of information.

---

[6]This "repeated measures" research design might be appropriate if the reliability of the measurement instrument in different environmental contexts is assessed and deemed to be acceptable.

For example, investigators who provide special training to persons who will be soliciting information from service recipients may enhance the inter-rater reliability of the outcome data. If these persons are held responsible for ensuring that all of the necessary information is collected, there will be less missing or incomplete data. Alternatively, if investigators use data that is compiled by untrained personnel or from data sources that are designed for other purposes (i.e., medical records), they should conduct an assessment to determine the completeness and accuracy of this information. Incomplete or inaccurate data is of little value.

The measurement of an outcome should be feasible from the perspective of providers and service recipients and can be achieved when investigators consider the workplace context within which data will be collected. In essence, the methods used to compile information should suit the workflow and organization of the clinical setting, as protocols that are disruptive will not receive the full cooperation of staff members. Data collection protocols that can be integrated into existing documentation and information systems will be more easily adopted. For example, it may be appropriate to use outcome indicators that are already being collected for other administrative purposes such as accreditation. Some health care organizations may have performance measures that they compile for the Joint Commission on Accreditation of Healthcare Organizations (JCAHO). JCAHO's ORYX initiative was established to integrate standardized, outcomes-related, performance measures into the accreditation process (JCAHO, 1998). Forer (1996) suggested that investigators consider using outcomes that are popular with other, similar providers to help organizations to contribute to standardized measurement systems and benchmark their performance.

Step 2: Compiling and Evaluating Evidence Regarding the Effect of a Service

Once the most relevant and important outcome indicators have been identified, investigators can progress toward compiling and evaluating evidence regarding the likelihood that an intervention or service influences these dimensions. It is important to evaluate the clinical effectiveness of an intervention when decision makers in health care organizations are determining whether to offer a new service or when a stakeholder group wants to evaluate a service that is currently offered. In both scenarios, investigators should review the literature to assess the strength of the evidence supporting the clinical effectiveness of similar interventions. However, in the second scenario, investigators must determine whether service recipients attain predefined outcomes due to their involvement in the program offered by a particular provider. Therefore, the second section of this chapter provides information on conducting a systematic review of the literature and selecting instruments to measure specific outcomes.

Literature Review

A review of the literature should be conducted during the planning stages of an evaluation when it is important to understand a particular issue and capitalize on what others have done (Evidence-Based Care Resource Group, 1994). This process helps investigators become more informed about the results of evaluations on similar interventions, the strengths and weaknesses of relevant methodological approaches, the importance of certain outcomes, and the psychometric soundness of potential measurement instruments. The experiences and thoughts of other investigators will assist in clarifying the nature and significance of the clinical problem and guide interpretation of the results (Abramson, 1990). However, the literature review should be an ongoing process that occurs throughout an evaluation.

Margolis and Petti (1994) illustrated the worth of conducting a literature review when they conducted a cost-benefit analysis to determine the value of offering a new service in a community. These investigators estimated financial figures (i.e., costs and economic benefits) in collaboration with local agencies and hospitals but determined typical usage rates and health outcomes after they conducted a review of the literature. An example of this approach to using the literature to estimate the value of an intervention is provided in the Practice Exercises in chapter 7.

There have been a tremendous number of articles that have been published in recent years regarding how to conduct a systematic review and critical appraisal of the literature. The Learning Resources section of this chapter provides a list of these references and offers information on how to locate electronic data sources. Journal publications, government documents, reports from healthcare organizations, and on-line databases are all sources of information regarding the effectiveness of medical interventions and the relative value of specific health services.

Since the late 1970s there has been a movement toward appraising the quality of evidence on the effectiveness of health interventions, and various authors have published classification systems regarding different levels of evidence and grades of recommendations (Canadian Task Force on the Periodic Health Examination, 1979; Center for Evidence-Based Medicine, 1998; Guyatt et al., 1995; United States Preventive Services Task Force, 1993). These taxonomies can be used to assist investigators in making judgments regarding the strength of support there is for the effectiveness of an intervention at attaining specific outcomes. Basically, evidence is rated high quality if has been derived from a randomized, controlled trial where participants are randomly recruited and assigned to treatment and control groups. Nonrandomized trials, controlled or cohort studies, case series, case-controlled or cross-sectional research designs are rated moderate quality. The expressed or written opinions of experts that are based on their experience, knowledge of the literature, and discussion with peers are rated low quality. Investigators who collaborate with the Agency for Health Care Policy and Research to develop clinical practice guidelines use levels of evidence when they appraise the literature. An example of the ranking system used by Gresham et al. (1995) in their guidelines for poststroke rehabilitation is provided in Box 4. Laupacis, Feeny, Detsky, and Tugwell (1992) and the Center for Evidence-Based Medicine (1998) offered approaches to applying these classification systems to appraise the quality of economic evaluations.

Although other researchers may have established the clinical effectiveness of an intervention in promoting certain outcomes, the applicability of these results to other populations and similar services may be limited. Investigators must make judgments regarding the extent to which findings can be generalized to similar persons or comparable services. The most important threats to external validity include the degree to which participants in the study are representative of persons in other jurisdic-

---

Box 4
Levels of Research Evidence (Gresham, Duncan, Stason, et al., 1995)

Level A
Supported by the results of two or more randomized controlled trials (RCTs) that have good internal validity and also specifically address the question of interest in a group of comparable patients (external validity)

Level B
Supported by a single RCT meeting the criteria given above for "A"-level evidence by RCTs that only indirectly address the questions of interest or by two or more nonrandomized clinical trials (case control or cohort studies) in which the experimental and control groups are demonstrably similar or multivariate analyses effectively controlled for group differences

Level C
Supported by a single nonRCT meeting the criteria given above for "B"-level evidence by studies using historical controls or by studies using quasi-experimental designs such as pre- and posttreatment comparisons

NA (not available)
Recommendation is not addressed by experimental studies

Expert Opinion
Strong consensus. Agreement among 90% or more of panel members and expert reviewers
Consensus. Agreement among 75% to 89% of panel members and expert reviewers

---

tions or populations and the degree to which other providers can replicate the situation in which participants in the treatment group were exposed (Shortell & Richardson, 1978).

Measuring Relevant Outcomes

Once the most relevant and important outcomes have been defined, investigators are challenged to select instruments to measure these concepts. Investigators may prefer to measure specific outcome variables using existing instruments (e.g., standardized assessments) or by creating new ones (e.g., customized questionnaires). It would seem that the most common mistakes made by investigators are to use an assessment tool they are familiar with rather than spend the effort required to discover a more appropriate instrument or to develop and use a tool whose psychometric properties are unknown. Information that is collected from an inappropriate measurement tool is of little value. Investigators who spend the time required to identify and learn a new instrument that was specifically designed to measure the outcome of interest are much better off than investigators who develop or use a tool whose psychometric properties are unknown. Law (1987) wrote an excellent article that provides information to assist clinicians in determining the scientific rigor and utility of a measurement instrument. At a minimum, all assessment tools should be selected on the basis of their content validity.

The selection of an instrument to measure an outcome requires a consideration of the tools' psychometric properties including its validity, reliability, sensibility, feasibility, and responsiveness (Deyo et al., 1994; Ferris & Norton, 1992). *Validity* refers to the ability of a tool to measure the concept it purports to measure. *Reliability* refers to the repeatability or reproducibility of results obtained with an assessment tool; it reflects the stability, consistency and dependability of a measure. Box 5 provides an overview of the different types of validity and reliability. *Sensibility* refers to whether the instrument is suited to the evaluation—whether it is applicable to the clientele and to the setting where service recipients will be recruited. An assessment instrument's *feasibility* refers to the ease and simplicity with which the data can be collected. The more feasible that an outcome is to measure, the more likely that the required data will be collected. *Responsiveness* refers to the sensitivity of a measurement tool or its ability to detect small but important changes. These dimensions of an instrument are essential to consider when selecting an assessment tool, as the quality of the results of an evaluation is only as good as the quality of the data used in the analysis.

Measurement instruments are used by investigators to collect information to profile or compare participants (i.e., description), to determine the probability of future events or certain traits (i.e., prediction), and to assess the effectiveness of treatment (i.e., evaluation). Assessments that are

Box 5
Reliability and Validity: Definitions and Types

Reliability
The repeatability or reproducibility of results and reflects the stability, consistency, and dependability of a measure

Types
1. *Internal consistency* refers to how well items in an instrument measure the same concept.
2. *Test-retest reliability* considers the stability of a measure over time.
3. *Interrater reliability* specifies the amount of error associated with the measurement process that is caused by individual scorers or raters.

Validity
How well or correctly an instrument adequately measures the concept under study

Types
1. *Content validity* refers to whether an instrument adequately covers the parameters, domains, or specific aspects of a concept. Content validity includes face and consensual validity.
   a. *Face validity* assesses whether the target population thinks the instrument measures what it is supposed to measure and is usually judged by external reviewers after an instrument is constructed.
   b. *Consensual validity* extends this process by having a panel of experts examine and rate the appropriateness of each item. Face and consensual validity provide methods by which to judge content validity (Green & Lewis, 1986).
2. *Criterion-related validity* refers to the degree to which information or scores on the instrument are correlated with some external criterion.
   a. *Predictive, criterion-related validity* uses a future criteria.
   b. *Concurrent, criterion-related validity* uses an alternative or existing criteria.
3. *Construct validity* refers to the extent to which hypothesized relationships can be verified on the basis of obtained data.

used for evaluative purposes attempt to measure change over time. Therefore, these instruments should demonstrate adequate content and construct validity, interrater and test-retest reliability, and responsiveness (Kirshner & Guyatt, 1985; Law, 1987). Appendix A lists a number of measurement instruments that are popular in the rehabilitation literature.

Economic Outcomes

As illustrated in the conceptual framework provided in Figure 2 in chapter 2, the outcomes of a health service can be health or economic. Whereas the majority of this chapter and the bulk of evaluations published in the literature focus on identifying and measuring health outcomes, the economic consequences that occur after a health service has been rendered are also important. These economic outcomes are conceptually distinct from the costs associated with the start-up and operation of a service in that the former reflects the financial events that occur as a result of (i.e., after) service recipients' participation in a health program. For example, consider the out-of-pocket expenses paid by consumers of a pain management program. Expenses paid by consumers in the form of copayments or deductibles are considered a cost whereas changes in out-of-pocket expenses that occur as a result of (i.e., after) participation in a health program (e.g., financial savings due to lower spending on pain medication) are considered an economic outcome.

Economic outcomes include those associated with alterations in the future employment earnings of service recipients, any positive or negative changes in the personal income or spending of service recipients, and any positive or negative changes in future expenditures on health. Box 6 provides three clinical examples illustrating the measurement and valuation of economic outcomes.

Cost-benefit analyses require that health outcomes be translated to monetary values or economic outcomes. Investigators who specialize in conducting this type of evaluation have employed estimates of willingness-to-pay or willingness-to-accept to translate health outcomes into monetary figures (Diener, O'Brien, & Gafni, 1997; O'Brien & Gafni, 1996; O'Brien & Viramontes, 1994). Willingness-to-pay has been proposed as a measure to quantify a person's willingness to pay for participation in a program, whereas willingness-to-accept could be used to measure the minimum a person would need to be compensated to forego involvement in a program (O'Brien & Viramontes, 1994). These estimates are then use to calculate the monetary value or economic implications of different health outcomes.

Summary

The effectiveness of a clinical intervention should be established before an assessment of costs as it would be inappropriate and wasteful to calculate the cost of providing ineffective services (Drummond et al., 1997). There are basically two steps to follow when assessing the effect of a clinical service: (a) the identification of important health and economic outcomes that are valued by all stakeholders, and (b) the compilation of evidence regarding the type and level of effect that an intervention has on service recipients. This chapter provides investigators with some insights as to how to select relevant outcomes and measurement instruments. Resources are provided for investigators who want to enhance their skills at reviewing and appraising evidence from the literature regarding the effectiveness of specific clinical interventions. Readers should review chapters 3 and 8 for basic information on how to conduct an evaluation to attribute outcomes to the

---

Box 6
Clinical Scenarios Illustrating the Measurement and Valuation of Economic Outcomes

---

Boyle, Torrance, Sinclair, and Horwood (1983) conducted a cost-benefit analysis to determine the relative value of offering versus not offering neonatal intensive care to very-low-birth-weight infants. These investigators calculated the net financial effect on society of this new approach to neonatal care by subtracting the additional cost of this intervention from the extra lifetime earnings that would accrue to infants who received intensive care. Notice that these investigators focused on the incremental costs and outcomes of intensive care; the comparison service was the delivery of less intensive care.

Rizzo, Baker, McAvay, and Tinetti (1996) conducted a cost-benefit analysis to determine the relative value of an intervention program that was being offered to reduce the frequency of falls among high-risk, elderly persons who lived in the community. These investigators calculated and compared the intervention costs with the financial savings (i.e., economic outcomes) that would accrue from reductions in expenditures on hospital, nursing home, and home health services. The effect of the intervention on health service usage rates was calculated by comparing a sample of participants who received the intervention with those who did not receive the service. Hospital fees were estimated using average per diem rates charged by preferred service delivery organizations for specific International Classification of Diseases, 9th Revision, Clinical Modification diagnosis and procedure codes. These rates were obtained from the hospital association in the state in which the study was conducted. Rizzo et al. (1996) also estimated the savings in nursing home care using the average fee per day of care charged by skilled and intermediate care facilities in the geographic location of service recipients. Information on average daily charges in these facilities was obtained from the Connecticut Department of Health Services. Savings from reductions in outpatient services were estimated using price tables that were employed by a health maintenance organization to assign charges to Current Procedural Terminology codes.

Margolis and Petti (1994) conducted a cost-benefit analysis to determine the relative value of offering a new intervention program to help children with significant, psychiatric disorders to receive home-based, family-centered intervention rather than inpatient care. These investigators estimated and compared the intervention costs of the new program with the financial savings that might accrue from reductions in expenditures on hospital services (i.e., economic outcomes). Financial estimates were made in collaboration with health care providers in the community, and usage rates were estimated using information derived from the literature.

receipt of a specific clinical service. Investigators who wish to develop their skill at conducting rigorous, clinical evaluations should consult the Learning Resources sections of these chapters. ❖

Practice Exercises

You have been asked to conduct an evaluation to assess the value of a program for women with fibromyalgia from the perspective of a health care organization. The program is currently offered over the course of 8 weeks, and it has been suggested that the number of sessions be reduced to five. After conducting interviews with clinical staff members and service recipients and reviewing documents provided by administration, you turn your thoughts to planning an investigation into the effectiveness of this service. Eventually, this information will be combined with costing data that has been compiled by a service provider. Refer to Box 3 in this chapter for more information about this clinical scenario and to Appendix D for responses to all questions.

1. What is the perspective of the analysis?
2. Cost-effectiveness analyses describe and compare the costs and outcomes of two or more health services. Describe the two service options being compared.
3. Identify possible health and economic outcomes that might be included in an evaluation.
4. Assume that all stakeholders have agreed that the services (i.e., 8-week and 5-week program) should be compared on the basis of their effectiveness at improving the functional status of service recipients in the area of basic activities of daily living. Identify the independent and dependent variables for this evaluation.
5. Recall from chapter 4 that a cost-effectiveness analysis provides the opportunity for investigators to make direct comparison between two or more interventions that affect service recipients in the same domain of health. On what basis can these two services be compared?
6. An instrument must be identified to measure the primary outcome of interest. What psychometric properties are important to assess when selecting this evaluation tool?

References

Abramson, J. H. (1990). *Survey methods in community medicine* (4th ed.). Edinburgh: Churchill Livingstone.

Boyle, M. H., Torrance, G. W., Sinclair, J. C., & Horwood, S. P. (1983). Economic evaluation of neonatal intensive care of very-low-birth-weight infants. *New England Journal of Medicine, 308*, 1330–1337.

Canadian Task Force on the Periodic Health Examination. (1979). The periodic health examination. *Canadian Medical Association Journal, 121*, 1193–1254.

Center for Evidence-Based Medicine. (1998, September 17). Levels of evidence and grades of recommendations. [Announcement posted on the World Wide Web]. Oxford, England: Author. Retrieved January 8, 1999, from the World Wide Web: www.cebm.jr2.ox.ac.uk/docs/levels.html

Deyo, R. A., Andersson, G., Bombardier, C., Cherkin, D. C., Kellerm R. B., Lee, C. K., Liang, M. H., Lipscomb, B., Shekelle, P., Spratt, K. F., & Weinstein, J. N. (1994). Outcome measures for studying patients with low back pain. *Spine, 19*, 2032S–2036S.

Diener, A., O'Brien, B., & Gafni, A. (1997). *Health care contingent valuation studies: A review and classification of the literature (Working Paper 07-06)*. Hamilton, Ontario: Centre for Health Economics and Policy Analysis.

Donabedian, A. (1980). *Explorations in quality assessment and monitoring: The definitions of quality and approaches to its assessment* (Vol.1). Ann Arbor, Michigan: Health Administration Press.

Drummond, M. F., O'Brien, B. J., Stoddart, G. L., & Torrance, G. (1997). *Methods for the economic evaluation of health care programmes* (2nd ed.). Oxford, UK: Oxford University Press.

Evidence-Based Care Resource Group. (1994). Evidenced-based care. Setting priorities: How important is this problem? *Canadian Medical Association Journal, 150*, 1249–1253.

Feldman, P. H., Latimer, E., & Davidson, H. (1996). Medicaid-funded home care for the frail elderly and disabled: Evaluating the cost savings and outcomes of a service delivery reform. *Health Services Research, 31*, 489–509.

Ferris, L. E., & Norton, P. G. (1992). Basic concepts in reliability and validity. In M. Stewart, F., Tudiver, M. J. Bass, E. V. Dunn, & P. G. Norton (Eds.), *Tools for primary care research* (pp. 64-76). London: Sage.

Forer, S. (1996). *Outcome management and program evaluation made easy: A toolkit for occupational therapy practitioners*. Bethesda, MD: American Occupational Therapy Association.

Green, L. W., & Lewis, F. M. (1986). *Measurement and evaluation in health education and health promotion*. Mountain View, CA: Mayfield.

Gresham, G. E., Duncan, P. W., Stason, W. B., et al. (1995). *Post-stroke rehabilitation: Clinical practice guideline* (AHCPR Publication No. 95-0662). Rockville, MD: United States Department of Health and Human Services, Public Health Service, Agency for Health Care Policy and Research.

Guyatt, G. H., Sackett, D. L., Sinclair, J. C., Hayward, R., Cook, D., & Cook, R. J. (1995). Users' guide to the medical literature: A method for grading health care recommendations. *Journal of the American Medical Association, 274*, 1800–1804.

Joint Commission on the Accreditation of Healthcare Organizations. (1998, June 15). ORYX: The next evolution in accreditation [Announcement posted on the World Wide Web]. Oakbrook Terrace, IL: Author. Retrieved August 4, 1998, from the World Wide Web: www.jcaho.org/perfmeas/oryx/oryx-qa.htm

Keith, R. A., (1995). Conceptual basis of outcome measures. *American Journal of Physical Medicine and Rehabilitation, 74*, 73–80.

Kirshner, B., & Guyatt, G. (1985). A methodological framework for assessing health and disease. *Journal of Chronic Disease, 38*, 27–36.

Kirz, H. L., & Larsen, C. (1986). Costs and benefits of medical student training to a health maintenance organization. *Journal of the American Medical Association, 256*, 734-739.

Kramer, A. M., (1997). Rehabilitation care and outcomes from the patient's perspective. *Medical Care, 35*(Supplement), JS48–JS57.

Langhorne, P., Wagenaar, R., & Partridge, C. (1996). Physiotherapy after stroke: More is better? *Physiotherapy Research International, 1*, 75–88.

Laupacis, A., Feeny, D., Detsky, A. S., & Tugwell, P. X. (1992). How attractive does a new technology have to be to warrant adoption and utilization? Tentative guidelines for using clinical and economic evaluations. *Canadian Medical Association Journal, 146*, 473–481.

Law, M. (1987). Measurement in occupational therapy: Scientific criteria for evaluation. *Canadian Journal of Occupational Therapy, 54*, 133–138.

Lohr, K. N. (1988). Outcomes measurement: Concepts and questions. *Inquiry, 25*, 37–50

Margolis, L. H., & Petti, R. D. (1994). An analysis of the costs and benefits of two strategies to decrease length of stay in children's psychiatric hospitals. *Health Services Research, 29*, 155–167.

Meyers, S. K. (1995). Exploring the costs and benefit drivers of clinical education. *American Journal of Occupational Therapy, 49*, 107–111.

Nagi, S. (1991). Disability concepts revisited: Implications for prevention. In A. M. Pope & A. R. Tarlov (Eds.), *Disability in America: Toward a national agenda for prevention*. Washington, DC: National Academy Press.

O'Brien, B., & Gafni, A. (1996). When do the "dollars" make sense? Toward a conceptual framework for contingent valuation studies in health care. *Medical Decision Making, 16*, 288–299.

O'Brien, B., & Viramontes, J. L. (1994). Willingness to pay: A valid and reliable measure of health state preference? *Medical Decision Making, 14*, 289–297.

Office of Technology Assessment. (1978). *Assessing the efficacy and safety of medical technologies*. Washington, DC: Congress of the United States, Office of Technology Assessment.

Orkin, F. K., Cohen, M. M., & Duncan, P. G. (1993). The quest for meaningful outcomes. *Anesthesiology, 78*, 417–422.

Rizzo, J. A., Baker, D. I., McAvay, G., & Tinetti, M. E. (1996). The cost-effectiveness of a multifactorial targeted prevention program for falis among community elderly persons. *Medical Care, 34*, 954–969.

Rush, B., & Ogborne, A. (1991). Program logic models: Expanding their role and structure for program planning and evaluation. *Canadian Journal of Program Evaluation, 6*, 95–106.

Shortell, S. M., & Richardson, W. C. (1978). *Health program evaluation*. St. Louis, MO: Mosby.

Stoddart, G. L. (1982). Economic evaluation methods and health policy. *Evaluation and the Health Professions, 5*, 393–414.

Torrance, G. W., Siegel, J. E., & Luce, B. R. (1996). Framing and designing the cost-effectiveness analysis. In M. R. Gold, J. E. Siegel, L. B. Russell, & M. C. Weinstein (Eds.), *Cost-effectiveness in health and medicine* (pp. 54–81). New York: Oxford University Press.

United States Preventative Services Task Force. (1993). Screening for adolescent idiopathic scoliosis: Review article. *Journal of the American Medical Association, 269*, 2667–2672.

Watson, D. E. (1997). *Task analysis: An occupational performance approach*. Bethesda, MD: American Occupational Therapy Association.

White House Domestic Policy Council. (1993). *Health security: The President's report to the American people*. Washington, DC: Author.

Whiteneck, G. G. (1994). Measuring what matters: Key rehabilitation outcomes. *Archives of Physical Medicine and Rehabilitation, 75*, 1073–1076.

World Health Organization. (1980). *International classification of impairments, disabilities, and handicaps: A manual of classification relating to the consequences of disease*. Geneva: Author.

Learning Resources

Clinical Evaluation

Campbell, D. T., & Stanley, J. C. (1966). *Experimental and quasi-experimental designs for research*. Skokie, IL: Rand McNally.

Cook, T. D., & Campbell, D. T. (1979). *Quasi-experimentation: Design and analysis issues for field settings*. Boston: Houghton Mifflin.

Critical Appraisal

Forchuk, C. & Roberts, J. (1993). How to critique qualitative research articles. *Canadian Journal of Nursing Research, 25*, 47–55.

Katz, R. T., Campagnolo, D. I., Goldberg, G., Parker, J. C., Pine, Z. M., & Whyte, J. (1995). Critical evaluation of clinical research. *American Journal of Physical Medicine and Rehabilitation, 76*, 82–93.

Krefting, L. (1991). Rigour in qualitative research: The assessment of trustworthiness. *American Journal of Occupational Therapy, 45*, 214–222.

Oxman, A. D. (1994). Checklists for review articles. *British Journal of Medicine, 309*, 648–651.

Shekelle, P. G., Andersson, G., Bombardier, C., Cherkin, D., Deyo, R., Keller, R., Lee, C., Liang, M., Lipscomb, B., Spratt, K., Weinstein, J. (1994). A brief introduction to the critical reading of the clinical literature. *Spine, 19*, 2028S–2031S.

Measurement in Rehabilitation Services

Fisher, W. P. (1993). Measurement-related problems in functional assessment. *American Journal of Occupational Therapy, 47*, 331–338.

Law, M. (1987). Measurement in occupational therapy: Scientific criteria for evaluation. *Canadian Journal of Occupational Therapy, 54*, 133–138.

Law, M., & Letts, L. (1989). A critical review of scales of activities of daily living. *American Journal of Occupational Therapy, 43*, 522–528.

Merbitz, C., Morris, J., & Grip, J. C. (1989). Ordinal scales and foundations of misinference. *Archives of Physical Medicine and Rehabilitation, 70*, 30–312.

Silverstein, B., Fisher, W. P., Kilgore, K. M., Harley, J. P., & Harvey, R. F. (1992). Applying psychometric criteria to functional assessment in medical rehabilitation: Defining interval measures. *Archives of Physical Medicine and Rehabilitation, 70*, 507–518.

Wood-Dauphinee, S., & Küchler, T. (1992). Quality of life as a rehabilitation outcome: Are we missing the boat? *Canadian Journal of Rehabilitation, 6*(1), 3–12.

Wright, B. D., & Linacre, J. M. (1989). Observations are always ordinal; measurements, however, must be interval. *Archives of Physical Medicine and Rehabilitation, 70*, 857–860.

Systematic Reviews and Electronic Databases

Bero, L., & Rennie, D. (1995). The Cochrane Collaboration: Preparing, maintaining and disseminating systematic reviews of the effects of health care. *Journal of the American Medical Association, 274*, 570–574.

Dickersin, K., Scherer, R., & Lefebrve, C. (1994). Identifying relevant studies for systematic reviews. *British Journal of Medicine, 309*, 1286–1291.

Elixhauser, A., Luce, B. R., Taylor, W. R., & Reblando, J. (1993). Health care CBA/CEA: An update on the growth and composition of the literature. *Medical Care, 31*(7 Supplement), JS1–JS11.

Findley, T. W., (1991). Research in physical medicine and rehabilitation: The conceptual review of the literature on how to read more articles than you ever want to see in your entire life. *American Journal of Physical Medicine and Rehabilitation, 70*, S17–S22.

Forchuk, C., & Roberts, J. (1993). How to critique qualitative research articles. *Canadian Journal of Nursing Research, 25*, 47–55.

Friede, A., Taylor, W. R., & Nadelman, L. (1993). On-line access to a cost-benefit/cost-effectiveness analysis bibliography via CDC WONDER. *Medical Care, 31*(7 Supplement), JS12–JS17.

Hayes, R., & McGrath, J. (1998). Evidence-based practice: The Cochrane Collaboration and occupational therapy. *Canadian Journal of Occupational Therapy, 65*, 144–151.

Oxman, A. D. (Ed.). (1994). Section VI: Preparing and maintaining systematic reviews. In *The Cochrane collaboration handbook.* Oxford, England: Cochrane Collaboration. This document is available on the World Wide Web at http://hiru.mcmaster.ca/COCHRANE/handbook/default.htm

Oxman, A. D., & Guyatt, G. H. (1988). Guidelines for reading literature reviews. *Canadian Medical Association Journal, 138*, 697–703.

Pollock, N. (1998). The Cochrane collaboration. *Canadian Journal of Occupational Therapy, 65*, 168–169.

The Cochrane Library offers electronic access to high quality evidence regarding health care interventions. The Cochrane Library includes the *Cochrane Database on Systematic Reviews*, the *Cochrane Clinical Trials Register*, the *Cochrane Review Methodology Database*, and the *Database of Abstracts of Reviews of Effectiveness*. The *Cochrane Database of Systematic Reviews* is a popular source of reviews regarding the efficacy and effectiveness of health care interventions. It contains a collection of regularly updated, systematic reviews that are primarily based on randomized controlled trials. The *Cochrane Clinical Trials Register* is an electronic bibliography of controlled trials that have been identified by contributors to the Cochrane Collaboration. It contains both published and unpublished research studies and represents an unbiased source of data for systematic reviews. The *Cochrane Review Methodology Database* is an electronic database of publications regarding the methods by which research can be critically appraised and synthesized. The *Database of Abstracts of Reviews of Effectiveness* (DARE) includes structured abstracts of systematic reviews from around the world. This database is maintained by the National Health Service Centre for Reviews and Dissemination at the University of York in England.

Access to The Cochrane Library is available through most university libraries. The CD-ROM version can be obtained by subscription from the BMJ Publishing Group. Hayes and McGrath (1998) and Pollock (1998) discussed the importance and utility of the Cochrane Database to occupational therapy. Refer to Bero and Rennie (1995) for more information on the Cochrane Collaboration. The Cochrane Collaboration site in the United States is at the University of Maryland School of Medicine, Department of Epidemiology and Preventative Medicine. Their World Wide Web site is at www.cochrane.org/

The National Health Service's (NHS) Centre for Reviews and Dissemination provides the results of systematic reviews and has the *Database of Abstracts of Reviews of Effectiveness* (DARE) and the *NHS Economic Evaluation Database* electronic databases available from the World Wide Web at www.york.ac.uk/inst/crd/

The Centers for Disease Control and Prevention (CDC) has developed an online bibliography on economic evaluations that have been conducted in the area of preventative health. This *Wide-Ranging On-Line Data for Epidemiologic Research* (CDC WONDER) is available to all public health professionals at no cost (Friede, Taylor, & Nadelman, 1993).

The National Library of Medicine offers access to 16 electronic databases including MEDLINE© through their Internet Grateful Med (IGM). The goal of offering access is to provide users with free assisted interactive retrieval from multiple information resources. The Library has recently made its IGM training manual available in PDF, PostScript and WordPerfect formats. This information is available from the World Wide Web at http://igm.nlm.nih.gov/

Refereed journals that have published economic evaluations between 1979 and 1990 include the *Journal of the American Medical Association* (JAMA), *New England Journal of Medicine*, *Social Science and Medicine*, and the *British Medical Journal* (BMJ).

7
Identifying the Costs of Clinical Services

In addition to cost containment, purchasers are looking for demonstrable value of the health care dollars they spend. (Davies et al., 1994, p. 8).

Learning Objectives

*   Describe the reasons why it is important to consider the cost of care when determining or demonstrating the value of a clinical service.
*   Identify the types of costs that are relevant to include in an economic evaluation.
*   Identify a variety of methods by which information on the cost of services can be collected.
*   Describe how financial and nonfinancial costs should be measured and valued.
*   Recognize that there are no standard rules guiding how resource contributions should be identified, measured, or valued.

Over the last few decades there has been growing concern over the size and rate of growth in national expenditures on health care in the United States and the value the public receives for each dollar spent on medical services. In 1996, the total cost of national health services surpassed $1 trillion, and these expenditures are expected to increase to $1.4 trillion by the year 2000 (Vincenzino, 1997). Expenditures on health services have increased faster than the rate of inflation and have outpaced growth in the gross domestic product since the 1940s (Koch, 1993). This means that Americans are able to spend less and less on other valuable goods and services as time passes. In 1990, the United States spent more on health care than on education and defense combined (White House Domestic Policy Council, 1993).

Despite spending more per capita than other industrialized countries on health and medical interventions, there is evidence that Americans do not receive value for the money they spend on these services. For example, in spite of these high expenditures, the United States ranks 19th in infant mortality, 21st in life expectancy for men, and 16th in life expectancy for women when compared with other countries in the world (White House Domestic Policy Council, 1993). In addition, it is often assumed that health care that is more costly is of higher quality than less expensive services, but research evidence does not confirm this relationship (Haas-Wilson, 1994; Starfield et al., 1994). There is substantial evidence that the amount of money that is spent on a person for specific health services depends on where they live in the country although no discernable differences in premorbid health or outcomes of patients justify the differences in costs (Lee, Huber & Stason, 1997; Miller & Levy, 1997). "The fundamental problem in America is not that we spend too little for health care. It is that we don't get *good value* for the billions of dollars we spend" (White House Domestic Policy Council, 1993, p. 10).

Determining which health services offer value to the American public requires that information be available regarding the costs and outcomes of comparable health care programs. Providing evidence regarding the effectiveness of therapeutic intervention is not adequate unless this information is coupled with an understanding of the resources required to provide a service and achieve a specific outcome. The economic evaluation methods described in this book provide a systematic approach by which the cost and outcomes of different interventions can be described and compared to help decision makers determine the relative value of these services.

The term *cost* in the context of economic evaluation refers to the amount or volume of resource contributions that are used for the delivery and consumption of a service. There are two types of costs to consider when conducting an evaluation: *financial* and *nonfinancial*. Although costs are typically valued using financial or monetary figures, some relevant and important resource contributions are nonfinancial or intangible. For example, the use of clinical practitioners to deliver a service represents a financial cost to health care providers. However, the use of volunteer workers to provide a service does not represent a direct financial expense to providers but reflects the consumption of a valuable resource. Therefore, the use of volunteers represents a nonfinancial or intangible resource contribution. If volunteers could not be recruited, paid workers might have to perform their duties. Alternatively, if the service was terminated the time donated by volunteers could be used to enhance other clinical programs. Table 7 provides definitions and examples of different types of costs.

Balas et al. (1998) developed a framework that investigators can use to report the costs associated with clinical interventions. This framework incorporates the accounting categories defined by the Panel on Cost-Effectiveness

Table 7
Different Types of Financial and Nonfinancial Costs (Anthony & Reece, 1989; Balas et al., 1998; Bischof & Nash, 1996)

Type of Cost	Definition	Example
Accounting cost	Costs that are administratively determined using various accounting principles	The overhead cost allocated to a department
Average cost	The cost of producing an average unit of service; these costs represent accounting figures not actual monetary expenses; see standard costs	The average cost of providing a splint as determined by the total cost of production divided by the number of splints
Direct cost	The costs associated with items that are specifically traced to, or caused by, the health service; the price of these resource contributions can be determined using market values	Fee-for-service cost to payers to provide a service to a health plan enrollee
Financial cost	Costs that can be valued using monetary currency	Out-of-pocket expenses, wages, charges
Fixed costs	The costs that do not change in the short term by a change in the volume of services provided	Equipment, tools, heating, rent, overhead, supervisor salaries
Full costs	The cost of all resources used to produce and consume a health service	All financial and nonfinancial costs of resource inputs
Incremental cost	The difference between the cost of alternative services or programs	The incremental cost of a service that costs $150 compared with an alternative service that costs $100 is $50

(continued)

87

Table 7 (continued)

Type of Cost	Definition	Example
Indirect cost	The elements of costs that are associated with the production or consumption of a service; it is usually not possible nor feasible to measure directly these resource contributions	The cost of research and development, clinical supervision, overhead, loss of leisure or productive time
Intangible costs	See nonfinancial costs	See nonfinancial costs
Marginal cost	The cost of the resources consumed by providing an additional unit of service	The cost of providing one additional splint from the provider perspective is the price of labor and splinting materials
Nonfinancial costs	Costs are incurred through the production or receipt of a service; these costs are not easily valued using monetary figures	Effort, pain, discomfort, dissatisfaction, suffering, anxiety, volunteer time, lost productivity
Opportunity cost	The cost of the lost opportunity to invest a sum in some other venture that yields positive results	The cost of using staff member time for activities other than revenue generation
Operating costs	Expenses associated with the day-to-day operation of the intervention program	Direct costs of labor and supplies as well as general overhead
Overhead	The indirect costs associated with the operation and "housing" of a program	Administrative fees and occupancy costs such as rent, utilities, and telephone
Standard cost	A measure of how much an item should have cost rather than an assessment of actual costs	The cost of providing typical intervention to a typical patient in the target population

(continued)

Table 7 (continued)

Type of Cost	Definition	Example
Start-up cost	Costs required for one-time development of an intervention	Labor associated with getting an intervention underway such as new equipment or space
Sunk cost	Costs that have already been spent	The cost that was paid to purchase equipment that has been used to provide a service; this does not include future replacement cost
Variable cost	The costs that vary, in total, directly and proportionately with changes in the volume of services delivered	The cost of materials and supplies

in Health and Medicine[7] that includes startup costs (e.g., labor, new equipment and space, consulting fees) and operating expenses such as direct costs of intervention and general overhead. The direct costs of intervention include the expenses associated with clinical and nonclinical support personnel and supplies, whereas general overhead includes administrative and occupancy costs. These authors used the financial figures published in an economic evaluation that was conducted by Oldridge et al. (1993) to demonstrate how their framework could be used to report the costs associated with a cardiac rehabilitation program.

There are basically two steps to follow when determining the cost of a clinical service. Step 1 involves identification of the most relevant and important resource contributions or costs to include in the analysis; Step 2 requires the measurement and valuation of these items. Once the cost of an intervention has been estimated, the next step to completing an economic evaluation is to combine this data with information regarding the outcomes of the service. When planning an evaluation, the effectiveness of

---

[7]The Panel on Cost-Effectiveness in Health and Medicine was convened by the Public Health Service in 1993 to develop a framework to standardize the analytical methods used in economic evaluations. The Panel published its findings in a journal article by Russell, Gold, Siegel, Daniels, and Weinstein (1996) and a book by Gold, Siegel, Russell, and Weinstein (1996).

an intervention should be established before any assessment of costs, as it would be inappropriate and wasteful to calculate the cost of providing ineffective services (Drummond, O'Brien, Stoddart, & Torrance, 1997).

Step 1: Identify the Resource Contributions

The Importance of Perspective

The most relevant resources that are consumed during the delivery and consumption of a service and, therefore, the most important costs to include in an economic evaluation are first identified by determining the perspective of the analysis. For example, from the societal viewpoint, all direct health care expenditures, social service fees, patient and family member expenses, and the costs associated with patients' time and care giving should be included.

Weinstein and Stason (1977) provided a conceptual model that can be used to identify the costs of a service from the societal perspective. Net costs are considered to be a function of the direct cost of medical and health care services (C_D), plus the costs associated with adverse side-effects of treatment (C_{SE}), less the savings associated with the prevention or alleviation of disease (C_P), plus the costs associated with the treatment of diseases that would not have occurred if the patient had not lived longer as a result of the original treatment (C_{LE}). In summary, net societal costs are equal to: $C_D + C_{SE} - C_P + C_{LE}$. Notice that the societal perspective requires the identification, measurement, and valuation of direct and indirect financial expenses as well as nonfinancial costs. Whereas the societal perspective has been recommended as the optimal viewpoint for a cost-effectiveness analysis (Russell, Gold, Siegel, Daniels, & Weinstein, 1996), the completion of a cost analysis from this viewpoint is complex and time consuming.

Most cost-effectiveness analyses that are published in the literature have been conducted from the viewpoint of the payer. From this perspective the most relevant and important resources used for the delivery and consumption of insured services are financial (i.e., charges levied by service providers and paid for by payers). From the service provider's perspective, the most relevant and important resources consumed to deliver a service are also financial (e.g., expenses associated with staff member time, materials, and overhead). By comparison, the patient perspective might include out-of-pocket expenses (i.e., financial costs) as well as the cost of time spent waiting for and receiving care (i.e., nonfinancial or intangible costs). Although there have not been many economic evaluations conducted from the patient's perspective, these analyses would typically include more intangible costs than evaluations that are conducted from the payer or service provider viewpoints. In summary, the resources used to deliver and consume a health service should be identified and described, and the scope of relevant costs can be determined by identifying the perspective of the analysis.

Incremental and Sunk Costs

Recall from chapter 4 that the results of a cost-effectiveness analysis are typically summarized using a ratio. The numerator of this ratio is computed by determining the differences in costs between two service alternatives (i.e., incremental costs), whereas the denominator is calculated by determining the differences in health outcomes between the services (i.e., incremental effectiveness). Therefore, when an investigator is conducting a cost assessment of two or more interventions, the differences in resource use between the services are the most relevant (Weinstein, Siegel, Gold, Kamlet, & Rusell, 1996).

Economic evaluations are often used to describe the full range of costs and outcomes of different health services. In this context, decision makers may be interested in the full cost of an intervention or the incremental cost of two or more services. Therefore, investigators should determine during the planning stages of an evaluation whether to calculate the full cost or incremental cost of each alternative. Box 7 provides an example to illustrate the relevance of incremental costs.

Persons who make decisions regarding the continuation, initiation, or termination of a health service are only interested in costs that will be incurred in the future. Historic or "sunk" costs are not relevant and should not be included in a cost assessment, as the decision to continue or abandon an existing service should not be made on the basis of money already spent. As these costs have already been incurred, they cannot be changed by any decision under current consideration (Anthony & Reece, 1989). Therefore, investigators who conduct economic evaluations should focus on identifying, measuring, and valuing costs that will be incurred in the future rather than historic expenditures that are irrecoverable.

In summary, the most relevant and important costs to consider when comparing two or more services are the incremental costs of each service that would be incurred in the future. However, some investigators conduct full cost assessments to provide decision makers with information on the range of resources required to implement a service. Although startup costs are important to consider when a new service may be implemented, historic expenditures are not relevant to any type of economic evaluation.

Methods of Data Collection

There are a number of different methods for collecting information to identify the most important and relevant costs to include in an evaluation. One method is to solicit this data directly from persons whose viewpoint will be used in the analysis. Traditional data collection methods such as interviews, focus groups, or questionnaires may be useful. For example, if the evaluation was conducted from the service provider perspective, it may be appropriate to solicit information from practitioners, clinical supervisors,

---

Box 7
Clinical Scenarios Illustrating the Relevance of
Incremental Costs

Consider a situation where an evaluator is comparing the cost-effectiveness of delivering a specific service to a defined clientele with a staff member complement of five occupational therapists (i.e., Service A) or a staff member complement of two occupational therapists and three occupational therapy assistants (i.e., Service B). The perspective selected for the evaluation is that of the health care provider. In 1997, the average annual salary of a full-time occupational therapist was $47,095 and the salary for an occupational therapy assistant was $31,126 (American Occupational Therapy Association, 1998). As employers must cover other employee expenses (e.g., health benefits), assume for this scenario that the average annual cost to service providers to employ an occupational therapist is $70,000 and the cost to employ an occupational therapy assistant is $50,000. In this context, the incremental cost or numerator of the cost-effectiveness ratio for Service A would equal 60,000.[8] Costs that remain the same under both scenarios are not incremental and do not need to be included in the ratio. The denominator of this ratio would include the incremental outcomes that accrue through the use of a staff member mix of five occupational therapists rather than two occupational therapists and three occupational therapy assistants.

Consider another situation where an evaluator is comparing the cost-effectiveness of delivering a specific service to a defined clientele five times per week (i.e., Service C) or three times per week (i.e., Service D). In this scenario, the incremental costs of providing services for 2 additional days per week are relevant. Costs that remain the same under both scenarios, such as the cost of the first three sessions in a week, are not incremental costs and do not need to be measured or valued unless decision makers want to understand the full cost to deliver a service. The numerator of the cost-effectiveness ratio of Service C would include the incremental cost of 2 days of service. The denominator of this ratio would include the incremental outcomes that accrue through the delivery of Service C rather than Service D.

---

[8]Recall from chapter 4 that the numerator of the cost-effectiveness ratio is equal to the total cost of a specific service minus the total cost of a comparison service. The annual cost of Service A is $350,000 (5 × $70,000) minus the annual cost of Service B or $290,000 (2 × $70,000 plus 3 × $50,000) equals $60,000. Therefore, the annual incremental cost of Service A equals $60,000.

administrators, and persons who work in accounting and finance. These persons could provide insight into the range of resources used to deliver the service as well as the quantity and price of these contributions.

An alternative source of information that can be used when the service provider or payer perspective has been selected is financial accounting (i.e., service provider viewpoint) or billing figures (i.e., payer viewpoint) from administrative databases. This information can be used to estimate the type, volume, and price of resources consumed to deliver a service. For example, Feldman, Latimer, and Davidson (1996) obtained Medicaid claims files and payroll data from various community agencies to identify the resources used to provide home care services. This information helped these investigators to compare two different methods of delivering home care to frail elderly and persons with disabilities. The cost assessment was conducted from the perspective of the payer.

In summary, Step 1 requires the identification of the different types of resources consumed during the delivery of a service. Investigators must first identify the perspective that will be used in the analysis then solicit information from persons in that audience regarding the quantity and price of relevant resource inputs. Secondary data sources such as administrative databases and published literature may also be useful. Whereas incremental costs are most relevant to decision makers who are comparing two or more services, some audiences of the final evaluation report may want to understand the full cost of delivering a service. In this context, investigators should estimate the incremental and full cost of the services that are being compared. Step 2 requires the measurement and valuation of these resource contributions.

Step 2: Measuring and Valuing Resources

The Importance of Perspective

The perspective of the analysis also affects the measurement and valuation of resource contributions. From the societal perspective, the volume of resources used to provide a health service should reflect average, standard, or typical consumption rates. In addition, the price per unit that is established for each contribution should reflect the market value of that particular resource. The use of average consumption rates and market prices ultimately improves the external validity of findings and the comparability of evaluations.

When the payer perspective is selected as the viewpoint of the analyses, costs are often measured using information on the charges rendered by service providers or prospectively determined rates. The amount that a service provider bills for a particular service (i.e., charges) may not resemble the amount of money that is actually paid to health care organizations because not all payers reimburse the full price (Finkler, 1982). The charges levied by service providers simply represent an accounting cost or administratively determined rates rather than the actual financial resources paid by payers. For example, when payments are made on a discounted fee-for-service basis, the monetary value that service providers charge does not represent the cost incurred by payers. When an evaluation is being conducted from the payer perspective, the actual amount paid is the relevant cost to include in the evaluation.

When the service provider perspective is employed, the cost to deliver a service could include either average or standard costs. *Average costs* reflect the average or mean cost to a specific service provider who has delivered services to a defined population, whereas *standard costs* reflect the amount that a service should have cost a typical service provider. The use of average costs requires that service providers collect and analyze their own financial information, whereas standard costs can theoretically be conducted by reviewing the literature or other external data sources regarding the typical quantity and price of resources consumed to deliver a service. An example of a cost assessment using standard costs and use rates derived from the literature is provided in Appendix D.

Financial Costs

The financial cost of a health service is a summary function of the volume of resources consumed and the unit price for each resource input. For example, the cost of the personnel resources required to deliver a service from the service provider perspective is the total amount of time that each staff member spends planning, managing, and delivering a service multiplied by the cost of each staff member's salary and benefits per time unit. Therefore, the full financial cost of a service is equal to the sum of the cost of each resource contribution, and this formula holds true irrespective of the viewpoint of the analysis.

External data sources such as the literature, community agencies, and administrative databases can be used to estimate standard consumption rates and the cost of various resource contributions. For example, the standard cost of therapy personnel for particular geographic regions or typical per diem rates for services can be obtained from national professional organizations, government departments, health service organizations, and community organizations. Margolis and Petti (1994) used standard costing methods and typical use rates to estimate the cost and benefits that might exist if services for children with significant psychiatric disorders was delivered using a home-based, family-centered approach. The comparison service was the delivery of inpatient care. Costs were estimated in collaboration with community agencies, and typical use rates were determined after the investigators conducted a literature review. Box 8 provides examples of clinical scenarios where investigators might use average consumption rates and standard costs.

Box 8
Clinical Scenarios Illustrating the Use of Average Consumption Rates and Standard Costs

Shalik (1987) conducted a cost-benefit analysis to determine the net financial effect of offering Level II fieldwork to occupational therapy students. The evaluation was conducted from the perspective of health care organizations, and the comparison service was the provision of no fieldwork opportunities. When conducting the cost assessment, the investigator estimated typical resource consumption (e.g., the amount of time that occupational therapists spent supervising students) by having a sample of students and supervisors maintain a diary to measure the amount of time they spent on educational activities. Interestingly, Shalik estimated the standard cost of this resource by using typical service provider charges. This method of valuation was selected as the amount of time that staff members spent with students that would otherwise be available to the health care organization for revenue generation. The investigator decided that the opportunity cost of providing supervision to students most closely reflected the financial charges billed by service providers. The financial benefits that accrued to service providers from having students deliver services were calculated using service provider charges.

Imagine that a specific service provider was interested in offering either intensive neurodevelopmental treatment or less intensive regular occupational therapy to children with cerebral palsy and wanted to make their decision on the basis of the relative cost-effectiveness of each intervention strategy. A review of the literature indicated that the relative effectiveness of these intervention alternatives was controversial. However, the service provider found a recent study (Law et al., 1997) that incorporated a rigorous methodological design to evaluate the effectiveness of these two intervention strategies. The study found no differences in outcomes in terms of hand function, quality of upper limb function, or parents' perceptions of performance. Whereas the two interventions produced similar outcomes, the resource contributions required to deliver these services differed greatly. Therefore, the service provider could use information regarding resource consumption provided by these investigators (e.g., the frequency and duration of therapy) and standard costs (e.g., state or national average occupational therapist wages) to evaluate the least costly service alternative (i.e., cost-minimization analysis). This information would also help this service provider to estimate the full cost of each service. Refer to the Practice Exercises for more information on this clinical scenario.

Information from administrative billing data can be used to assess the cost of services from the service provider perspective by using cost-to-charge ratios that are available from Medicare cost reports. These ratios help investigators to estimate the cost to a typical service provider. For example, Williams (1996) used cost-to-charge ratios to calculate the direct and indirect costs of supplies, pharmacy, laboratory, radiology, and miscellaneous items. This information was used to determine the cost to service providers offering emergency department services to persons who seek nonurgent care. Shwartz, Young, and Siegrist (1995) found that cost-to-charge ratios were more accurate when used to determine the cost of delivering care to a homogeneous group of service recipients, such as a diagnosis-related group, rather than the actual cost of delivering care to a person.

It is often more feasible to evaluate the direct costs of delivering a service than to measure and value the indirect costs associated with the delivery of a service. Indirect costs, such as institutional overhead, are more complex to measure and may require that investigators seek the assistance of an accountant. Most economic evaluations that have been published in the literature have been conducted by research teams, and these multidisciplinary groups often include persons who have accounting or finance backgrounds (Watson & Mathews, 1998). Sensitivity analysis can also be conducted to estimate the range within which the true cost of delivering a service falls. A more thorough discussion of this topic is provided in chapter 8.

Nonfinancial Costs

Although the production and consumption of health services are associated with a number of nonfinancial costs, the measurement and valuation of these intangible costs are particularly difficult and represent areas of controversy. For example, it is difficult to place a value on the time that caregivers and volunteers contribute to the care of service recipients. The measurement and valuation of caregiver time may be particularly important when comparing the cost-effectiveness of institutional versus home health care when the latter service requires that family members provide more direct care to service recipients. It is important to incorporate the cost of this resource when the economic evaluation is conducted from the societal perspective. Arguably, the unit price of family members' time is equivalent to the wage rate of a substitute worker. Alternatively, it could be argued that the unit price of caregiver time should equal the wage foregone by the family member or the average wage for their age and gender cohort. Whatever the decision, the analysis should be conducted under a number of assumptions regarding the cost of this resource.

To enhance the standardization of cost-effectiveness analyses, the Public Health Services' Panel on Cost-Effectiveness of Health and Medicine provided guidelines regarding the issue of placing a value on time (Luce, Manning, Seigel, & Lipscomb, 1996). The Panel advocated that the costs of delivering a health service, or the numerator of a cost-effectiveness ratio, should only include the costs of the patients' time due to seeking treatment. In addition, any consequences or effects that accrue after receipt of a health service (e.g., changes in the amount of time spent sick), or the denominator of a cost-effectiveness ratio, should be captured in quality of life measures. In addition, the cost of time should be valued using the wage rate for the age and gender composition of the target population (Weinstein et al., 1996). Readers who are interested in this issue of valuing time gained or lost should also review the journal article by Brouwer, Koopmanschap, and Rutten (1997).

Summary

There are basically two steps to follow when conducting a cost assessment for an economic evaluation. Step 1 involves the identification of the most relevant and important resource contributions or costs to include in the analysis; Step 2 requires the measurement and valuation of these items. The perspective of the analysis must be considered when determining which resource inputs are most relevant to the evaluation and how these costs should be measured and valued.

The most relevant resources associated with the production and consumption of a health service and the cost of these contributions can be identified using either primary (i.e., persons whose perspective will be used in the analysis) or secondary (e.g., administrative databases, literature) sources. Full costs are most relevant when determining the total cost of service alternatives whereas incremental costs are most relevant when comparing alternative interventions. The costs of resources that will be used in the future are most relevant to include in an analysis when making decisions regarding the continuation, initiation, or termination of a service. Historic costs are irrelevant as they cannot be changed by decisions under current consideration. Although it is often feasible to identify, measure, and value the direct financial costs of a service, inclusion of indirect financial costs in an evaluation may require the assistance of an accountant.

The valuation of costs that occur in the distant future or intangible costs such as time spent or gains or losses in the productivity of service recipients are particularly difficult to calculate and represent areas of controversy. Those who are interested in learning more about these areas of evaluation should consult the Learning Resources section of this chapter, chapter 8, and Appendix B. Although there are no standard rules guiding how to conduct a cost assessment, national guidelines have been established to address some of the more complex methodological issues (Canadian Coordinating Office for Health Technology Assessment, 1997; Luce et al., 1996). ❖

Practice Exercises

Imagine that you are interested in offering either an intensive neurodevelopmental treatment program or less intensive regular occupational therapy program to children with cerebral palsy. You must decide which service to offer and want to make your decision on the basis of the relative value of each intervention strategy.[9] As your department already has all of the equipment to deliver each service, there will not be any startup or initial investment costs. Refer to Appendix D for responses to the following questions.

1. You have obtained a copy of a study conducted by Law et al. (1997). Law et al. (1997) indicated that children in the intensive neurodevelopmental treatment group received twice-weekly therapy for 45 min over the course of 4 months, a 30-min daily home program, and a bivalved upper-extremity cast that was intended to be worn for a minimum of 4 hr/day on at least two separate occasions (i.e., Service A). You are conducting a cost-consequence analysis of this service from the service provider perspective. Use Table 8 to identify the relevant resource inputs and to estimate the full cost to deliver this service. At this point in the analysis include the cost of equipment and overhead.

2. Law et al. (1997) indicated that children who received less intensive, regular occupational therapy received services once a week for 45 min (i.e., Service B) over the course of 4 months. You are conducting a cost-consequence analysis of Service B from the service provider perspective. Use Table 9 to compute the financial cost to deliver this service. At this point in the analysis include the cost of equipment and overhead.

3. Persons who make decisions regarding the continuation, initiation, or termination of a health service are only interested in costs that will be incurred in the future, as historic or "sunk" expenditures cannot be recovered. If a service provider is interested in offering a service, startup costs such as those required to purchase new equipment should be included in the analysis. However, if equipment has already been purchased, the expenditures associated with the initial acquisition of this resource are irrelevant to the decision as to whether to offer a service in the future. However, replacement costs that occur in the future are relevant. Therefore, what expenditures identified in Tables 8 and 9 are relevant to decision makers?

4. Law et al. (1997) found no significant differences in outcomes between the two services in terms of children's hand function, quality of upper

---

[9]It is important to note that studies that incorporate cost measures into their design are likely a better job of estimating expenditures than studies that assess these expenses as an afterthought (Balas et al. 1998).

Table 8
A Cost Assessment: Service Provider's Costs to Deliver Intensive Neurodevelopmental Treatment

Step 1. Identify Resource Contributions	Step 2. Measure and Value the Resource Contributions Consumed			
	Quantity of Contributions Consumed To Deliver the Service (Q)	Price per Unit (P)	Cost of Contributions (Q × P)	Subtotal
1. Labor costs				
A. Clinical				
Evaluation				
Intervention				
Indirect[a]				
B. Administrative support				
			Total labor:	$
2. Material costs				
			Total material:	$
3. Equipment costs				
			Total equipment:	$
4. Other				
			Total other:	$
			FULL COST	$

[a]Indirect labor refers to time spent to prepare or document assessment and intervention.

limb function, and parents' perceptions of performance. Although Service A and Service B produced similar outcomes, the resource inputs required to deliver these services differed significantly.

  a. What would be the incremental cost to a service provider for offering Service A versus Service B?

  b. If the incremental benefits of Service A versus Service B are not significant, what type of economic evaluation have you just conducted?

    As a large portion of the cost estimate in Tables 8 and 9 are based on assumptions regarding the cost of certain resources, a sensitivity analysis will be conducted on this assessment in the Practice Exercises in chapter 8.

Table 9
A Cost Assessment: Service Provider's Costs to Deliver Regular Occupational Therapy Treatment

Step 1. Identify Resource Contributions	Step 2. Measure and Value the Resource Contributions Consumed			
	Quantity of Contributions Consumed To Deliver the Service (Q)	Price per Unit (P)	Cost of Contributions (Q × P)	Subtotal
1. Labor costs				
A. Clinical				
Evaluation				
Direct intervention				
Indirect[a]				
B. Administrative support				
Total labor: $				
2. Material costs				
Total material: $				
3. Equipment costs				
Total equipment: $				
4. Other				
Total other: $				
FULL COST $				

[a]Indirect labor refers to time spent to prepare or document assessment and intervention.

References

American Occupational Therapy Association. (1998, January 29). Salary data for profession available. *OT Week*, 6.

Anthony, R. N., & Reece, J. S. (1989). *Accounting text and cases* (8th ed.). Homewood, IL: Irwin Inc.

Balas, E. A., Kretschmer, R. A. C., Gnann, W., West, D. A., Boren, S. A., Centor, R. M., Nerlich, M., Gupta, M., West, T. D., & Soderstrom, N. S. (1998).

Interpreting cost analyses of clinical interventions. *Journal of the American Medical Association, 279,* 54–57.

Bischof, R. O., & Nash, D. B. (1996). Cost-effectiveness and cost containment: A physician's primer. In R. L. Perkel, & R. C. Wender (Eds.), *Primary care: Clinics in office practice. Models of ambulatory care* (pp. 115–127). Philadelphia: W. B. Saunders.

Brouwer, W. B., Koopmanschap, M. A., & Rutten, F. F. (1997). Productivity costs measurement through quality of life? A response to the recommendations of the Washington Panel. *Health Economics, 6,* 253–259.

Canadian Coordinating Office for Health Technology Assessment. (1997). *Guidelines for economic evaluation of pharmaceuticals: Canada* (2nd ed.). Ottawa, Ontario: Author.

Davies, A. R., Thomas Doyle, M. A., Lansky, D., Rutt, W., Orsolits Stevic, M., & Doyle, J. B. (1994). Outcomes assessment in clinical settings: A consensus statement on principles and best practices in project management. *Journal on Quality Improvement, 20,* p. 8. Oakbrook Terrace, IL: Joint Commission on Accreditation of Healthcare Organizations.

Drummond, M. F., O'Brien, B. J., Stoddart, G. L., & Torrance, G. (1997). *Methods for the economic evaluation of health care programmes* (2nd ed.). Oxford, UK: Oxford University Press.

Feldman, P. H., Latimer, E., & Davidson, H. (1996). Medicaid-funded home care for frail elderly and disabled: Evaluating the cost savings and outcomes of a service delivery reform. *Health Services Research, 31,* 489–508.

Finkler, S. A. (1982). The distinction between cost and charges. *Annals of Internal Medicine, 96,* 102–109.

Gold, M. R., Siegel, J. E., Russell, L. B., & Weinstein, M. C. (1996). *Cost-effectiveness in health and medicine.* New York: Oxford University Press.

Haas-Wilson, D. (1994). The relationships between the dimensions of health care quality and price: The case of eye care. *Medical Care, 32,* 175–182.

Koch, A. L. (1993). Financing health services. In S. J. Williams & P. R. Torrens (Eds.), *Introduction to health services* (4th ed.) (pp. 299–331). Albany, NY: Delmar.

Law, M., Russell, D., Pollock, N., Rosenbaum, P., Walter, S., & King, G. (1997). A comparison of intensive neurodevelopmental therapy plus casting and a regular occupational therapy program for children with cerebral palsy. *Developmental Medicine and Child Neurology, 39,* 664–670.

Lee, A. J., Huber, J. H., & Stason, W. B. (1997). Factors contributing to practice variation in post-stroke rehabilitation. *Health Services Research, 32,* 197–221.

Luce, B. R., Manning, W. G., Seigel, K. E., & Lipscomb, J. (1996). Estimating costs in cost-effectiveness analysis. In M. R. Gold, J. E. Siegel, L. B. Russell, & M. C. Weinstein (Eds.), *Cost-effectiveness in health and medicine* (pp. 176–213). New York: Oxford University Press.

Margolis, L. H., & Petti, R. D. (1994). An analysis of the costs and benefits of two strategies to decrease length of stay in children's psychiatric hospitals. *Health Services Research, 29,* 155–167.

Miller, T. R., & Levy, D. T. (1997). Geographic variation in expenditures for workers' compensation physician claims. *American Journal of Industrial Medicine, 32*(1), 27–34.

Oldridge, N., Furlong, W., Fenny, D., Torrance, G., Guyatt, G., Crowe, J., & Jones, N. (1993). Economic evaluation of cardiac rehabilitation soon after acute myocardial infarction. *American Journal of Cardiology, 72,* 154–161.

Russell, L. B., Gold, M. R., Siegel, J. E., Daniels, N., & Weinstein, M. C. (1996). The role of cost-effectiveness analysis in health and medicine. *Journal of the American Medical Association, 276,* 1172–1177.

Shalik, L. D. (1987). Cost-benefit analysis of Level II fieldwork in occupational therapy. *American Journal of Occupational Therapy, 41,* 638–645.

Shwartz, M., Young, D. W., & Siegrist, R. (1995). The ratio of costs to charges: How good a basis for estimating costs? *Inquiry, 32,* 476–481.

Starfield, B., Powe, N. R., Weiner, J. R., Stuart, M., Steinwachs, D., Scholle, S. H., & Gerstenberger, A. (1994). Costs vs. quality in different types of primary care settings. *Journal of the American Medical Association, 272,* 1903–1908.

Vincenzino, J. V. (1997). Trends in medical care cost—revisited. *Statistical Bulletin—Metropolitan Insurance Companies, 78*(3), 10–16.

Watson, D. E., & Mathews, M. (1998). Economic evaluation of occupational therapy: Where are we at? *Canadian Journal of Occupational Therapy, 65,* 160–167.

Weinstein, M. C., Siegel, J. E., Gold, M. R., Kamlet, M. S., & Russell, L. B. (1996). Recommendations of the Panel on Cost-Effectiveness in Health and Medicine. *Journal of the American Medical Association, 276,* 1253–1258.

Weinstein, M. C., & Stason, W. B. (1977). Foundations of cost-effectiveness analysis for health and medical practices. *New England Journal of Medicine, 296,* 716–721.

White House Domestic Policy Council. (1993). *Health security: The President's report to the American people.* Washington, DC: Author.

Williams, R. M. (1996). The costs of visits to emergency departments. *New England Journal of Medicine, 334,* 642–646.

Learning Resources

Balas, E. A., Kretschmer, R. A. C., Gnann, W., West, D. A., Boren, S. A., Centor, R. M., Nerlich, M., Gupta, M., West, T. D., & Soderstrom, N. S. (1998). Interpreting cost analyses of clinical interventions. *Journal of the American Medical Association, 279,* 54–57.

Drummond, M. F., O'Brien, B., Stoddart, G. L., & Torrance, G. W. (1997). Cost analysis. In M. F. Drummond et al. *Methods for the economic evaluation of health care programmes* (2nd ed.). New York: Oxford University Press.

Finkler, S. A. (1982). The distinction between cost and charges. *Annals of Internal Medicine, 96,* 102–109.

Grady, M. L., & Weis, K. A. (Eds.). (1995). *Cost analysis methodology for clinical practice guidelines.* Rockville, MD: United States Department of Health and Human Services.

Koopmanschap, M. A., & Rutten, F. F. (1996). A practical guide for calculating indirect costs of disease. *PharmacoEconomics, 10*, 460–466.

Krahn, M., & Gafni, A. (1993). Discounting in the economic evaluation of health care interventions. *Medical Care, 31*, 403–418.

Shwartz, M., Young, D. W., & Siegrist, R. (1995). The ratio of costs to charges: How good a basis for estimating costs? *Inquiry, 32*, 476–481.

Wolff, N., Helminiak, T. W., & Kraemer Tebes, J. (1997). Getting the cost right in cost-effectiveness analyses. *American Journal of Psychiatry, 154*, 736–743.

8
Enhancing Methodological Rigor

We all hear about the need for information on what kind of care is worth providing in terms of both costs and final results for the patient.... Outcomes research is still relatively new; its methods and applications are in the process of being developed and tried.... studies must be designed to fill its specific purpose, data must be valid and reliable with the specific purpose in mind, and information must be applied wisely. (Ellek, 1996, p. 886–889)

Learning Objectives
- Identify methodological elements for strengthening an evaluation project.
- Apply design and methodological considerations when reviewing existing studies.

The design and implementation of an economic evaluation are complex processes. They require that investigators understand and systematically apply methods to assess costs and outcomes and attribute these events toward the production and consumption of a specific health intervention. In addition, the expertise required to do these activities have traditionally been within the realm of accountants and researchers. Times are changing. The current marketplace now requires that all service providers have a basic understanding of the cost and outcomes of the services they deliver and apply these concepts when appraising evidence in the literature regarding the value of other interventions. In 1996, Ellek acknowledged that "outcomes research is still relatively new; its methods and applications are in the process of being developed and tried" (p. 889). This statement is as true today as it was then.

The chapters in this book have been designed to provide current and future health care practitioners and administrators with introductory information regarding how to appraise the costs and outcomes of different interventions. The purpose of this chapter is to build on this foundation and address some of the more complex and thorny methodological issues inherent in conducting economic evaluations. This information can be used when implementing or appraising an evaluation.

Research Question

Evaluations should begin with a statement that identifies and describes the focus and scope of the assessment. As with experimental research, these narratives should clearly and explicitly define the independent and dependent variables. In the context of an economic evaluation, the health service delivered by providers represents the independent variable, whereas the resource contributions or costs as well as the health and economic outcomes represent the dependent variables. A discussion regarding the phraseology of a good research question is provided in chapter 3.

Independent Variables

Evaluations may examine important clinical issues, innovative interventions, controversial treatments, or the delivery of care in novel settings. Whereas cost-consequence analyses can be used to describe or compare one or more interventions, all other forms of economic evaluation are used to compare the relative value of two or more programs. One of the services being compared may be the "no service" alternative, which is equivalent to the control group used in experimental research. Good studies describe the services that are being compared in sufficient detail so as to help another investigator to replicate the study (Drummond, O'Brien, Stoddart, & Torrance, 1997; Shekelle et al., 1994). The final report should include details regarding the intensity, frequency, and duration of care. It may be appropriate to document the experience and background of clinicians who deliver services as well as describe the setting in which the intervention is provided. This is particularly important if investigators determine or suspect that these factors significantly influenced the results of the study. When the evaluation focuses on a specific impairment or disability, diagnostic criteria must be stated, and all other inclusion and exclusion criteria should be defined.

Information regarding the services being evaluated is helpful to persons who will be reading the final report; particularly if they will be making judgments regarding the external validity of findings (Hoffman, Turner, Cherkin, Deyo, & Herron, 1994). *External validity* refers to the extent to which findings can be generalized to similar persons or comparable services. The most important threats to external validity include the degree to which participants in the study are representative of persons in other jurisdictions or populations and the degree to which other service providers can replicate the situation in which participants in the treatment group were exposed (Shortell & Richardson, 1978).

Dependent Variables

Good studies identify all of the relevant costs as well as the health and economic outcomes, even though not all of them may be incorporated into the analysis (Drummond et al., 1997; Torrance, Siegel, & Luce, 1996). It is appropriate to provide a rationale as to why certain costs and outcomes were included in the analysis and the process by which the most relevant costs and outcomes were selected. Chapters 6 and 7 provide information to assist investigators in identifying the most significant dependent variables.

The costs and outcomes selected for inclusion in the evaluation should be congruent with the perspective used in the analysis, appropriate to the type of economic evaluation conducted, and in alignment with the priorities of the target population. Superior studies demonstrate a clear and logical conceptual link between the intervention and the outcome. If multidimensional outcomes such as functional or health status are used, investigators would clarify which components were expected to change as a result of participation in a program. For example, functional status includes such things as basic and instrumental activities of daily living. The domain of functional status addressed by the intervention and included in the evaluation should be specified. Investigators should indicate when and how outcomes were measured and include a brief summary regarding the psychometric soundness of the assessment tools used to measure these concepts.

Study Design

The design of a study lays the road map for the evaluation and the analysis. This road map should be devised in the planning stages to avoid unexpected detours. Clinical evaluations that have the strongest methodological rigor have an experimental research design (i.e., randomized controlled trial). Participants in these studies are randomly selected from a target population and assigned to treatment and control groups. In addition, testers are trained, blinded, and randomly assigned to participants. In most clinical and rehabilitation settings, the implementation of an experimental design is not viable, so investigators use observational or quasi-experimental research designs. Katz et al. (1995) wrote an excellent article regarding different research designs to assist rehabilitation practitioners in appraising and implementing clinical research.

The research design used by investigators has a direct influence on the internal validity of the evaluation. *Internal validity* refers to the extent to which costs and outcomes are attributable to the service rather than competing explanations (Shortell & Richardson, 1978). Therefore, it is important to explicitly state the type of research design used to understand the shortcomings inherent in different designs and to acknowledge these limitations in the final report.

The most common research designs used in observational research are the "one-shot" case study and the "one group" pretest–posttest design (Shortell & Richardson, 1978). The one-shot case study involves having persons complete a questionnaire after they have received an intervention. For example, service recipients could complete a satisfaction questionnaire after receiving care. There are a number of reasons why survey results obtained using this strategy may not be valid. Participants may have experienced an event other than the service that influenced their level of satisfaction (i.e., history effects). In addition, the results could be attributable to systematic changes going on within program participants themselves (i.e., maturation effects).

The one group pretest–posttest is also a popular research design that is used in clinical settings. This approach requires that investigators measure the degree of change in service recipients by assessing them before and after they receive care. Again, there are a number of reasons why survey results obtained using this strategy may not be valid. In addition to the historical and maturation effects described above, the knowledge or experiences that participants receive while completing the pretest may also influence their performance on the posttest (i.e., testing effect). Additionally, any change in the persons who administer the questionnaires or the measures used to assess the outcomes may influence the results (i.e., instrumentation effects).

The results obtained from the one-shot case study and the one group pretest–posttest may hold more validity if the same findings are evident when these research designs are implemented with more than one cohort of service clientele or during multiple time periods. There are alternative quasi-experimental research designs that have been used to evaluate health interventions such as the nonequivalent control group (i.e., selection of a second group that is as similar as possible to the treatment group) and the time series design (i.e., multiple measures before and after receiving an intervention) (Campbell & Stanley, 1966). When investigators compare two different services that are already being provided to determine the relative value of each approach, this type of research design is similar conceptually to the nonequivalent control group. For example, Johnston and Miller (1986) conducted an economic evaluation using a nonequivalent control group design when they assessed the Health Care Financing Administration (HCFA) requirement that persons who obtain inpatient rehabilitation through the Medicare program receive therapy at least 3 hr/day. Clients who received rehabilitation services before the HCFA regulation (i.e., analogous to a control group) were compared with persons who received care after the regulation (i.e., treatment group).

Participants: Selection and Assignment

Sample Selection

Because it is impossible to solicit information from all persons who receive an intervention, a sample of participants is examined. There are a number of sampling strategies that can be used by investigators, but samples that are drawn using random or stratified random techniques are more representative and help investigators to make more valid generalizations. In order that others can make judgments regarding the representative of the sample used in the evaluation, investigators should explicitly state any inclusion and exclusion criteria used to select participants as well as the methods used to recruit these persons.

Good evaluations account for all persons who entered into the study. Often, participants who are included in an evaluation may not complete the assessment process. This loss in numbers, termed *attrition*, may be due to either very good or very bad outcomes (Hoffman et al., 1994). Persons who recover early in the study may drop out because they no longer feel the treatment is required. Alternatively, those who fare poorly may be discouraged and drop out. The sickest participants may die. Attrition is particularly problematic if it is greater or systematically different within one group than the other, thereby biasing the results. With substantial attrition rates, there is less confidence in the results. Attrition of greater than 20% threatens the validity of the conclusions (Shekelle et al., 1994). Therefore, the number of persons that were approached to be included in the evaluation, the number of persons who participated in the study, and the number of participants used in the analysis should be documented and sources of selection bias discussed. For example, the deliberate exclusion of certain persons, such as those who are very ill, may be a source of selection bias. This strategy may ultimately influence cost and outcome data. Any information that is available on persons who chose not to participate should be collected. This data can be used to test for significant differences between persons who were included in the evaluation and those who were not.

Sample Assignment

As mentioned throughout this book, most economic evaluations are conducted to compare the relative value of two or more services. Although randomization is the best method to employ to select participants from a population and assign persons to the different interventions, this may not always be feasible. However, random assignment should be used wherever possible as this strategy should minimize baseline differences between groups. For example, Rich et al. (1995) randomly assigned cardiac patients to treatment and control groups to assess the cost-effectiveness of a multidisciplinary intervention directed toward reducing hospital readmission rates. Rizzo, Baker, McAvay, and Tinetti (1996) randomly assigned persons to an intensive, fall prevention intervention or "usual care" to assess the cost-effectiveness of a service that was designed to reduce fall-related injuries in the elderly. These investigators all randomized participants to different treatment or control settings to ensure that the groups were homogeneous during the baseline time period. Homogeneity in groups is necessary when investigators want to attribute differences in outcomes between groups toward the receipt of health services rather than preexisting factors (Hoffman et al., 1994).

When it is not feasible to randomly assign persons to the services that are being compared in an evaluation, investigators may decide to use participants as their own control. For example, Law et al. (1997) used a randomized crossover design to assess the relative effectiveness of two intervention approaches that are used in clinical practice to enhance hand function among children with cerebral palsy. Alternatively, investigators can deliberately match two persons, one of whom receives an intervention while the other receives the comparison service. Katz et al. (1995) argued that it is too difficult to adequately match participants in rehabilitation programs. Investigators might compare two different services using a purely observational research design.

Investigators who are not able to randomly assign persons to the various services being evaluated are challenged to attribute differences in costs and outcomes toward the receipt of an intervention rather than to preexisting or case-mix differences between persons. These case-mix differences between persons in various groups may have a direct influence on costs and outcomes and bias results. For example, suppose two approaches to head injury rehabilitation were being compared but one service included persons who were much younger. As age is generally considered to be a determinant of neurological recovery, this variable may account for some of the lower costs and better outcomes attained by the service with younger recipients. In this scenario, case-mix differences in age could account for differences in costs and outcomes.

When participants are randomly assigned to intervention and control group conditions in experimental research designs, baseline differences between groups are minimized. This randomization process is not always feasible in clinical settings, therefore, investigators must always report the characteristics of persons who are ultimately included in each sample of service recipients. Information should be provided on age, gender, diagnoses, comorbid conditions, clinical symptomatology, stage of recovery, severity of illness, and other variables that may have a bearing on the results. Shekelle et al. (1994) suggested that investigators provide as much detail as occupational therapists would routinely provide when describing clients to their colleagues. These details will assist persons who read the final report in interpreting the comparability of the groups and the applicability of the findings to other populations. In addition, this information can be used in multivariate models to statistically control for differences in case-mix amongst the groups being compared.[10]

---

[10]Case-mix adjustment is required if any comparison of outcomes is made between different services, as factors other than the intervention (e.g., patient characteristics) can affect outcomes. This type of risk adjustment attempts to isolate the effect of patients' characteristics from the effect of treatments so that outcomes can be attributed to health services. Refer to the Learning Resources section for information on case-mix or risk adjustment.

In summary, random selection and assignment of persons enhances the external and internal validity of an evaluation respectively. Participants in an evaluation who are randomly selected from all service recipients are likely to be representative of these persons. When these participants are randomly assigned to groups, investigators are able to attribute differences in costs and outcomes to the receipt of health services rather than inequalities in case-mix. In clinical contexts, investigators are usually not able to randomly select and assign persons to groups. In these situations, the strategies used to recruit participants must be explained and the characteristics of the persons who participate in the different services that are being compared must be described. Any sources of selection bias or known differences in case-mix should be made explicit and accounted for in the analysis. Investigators who use multivariate analyses to test for significant treatment effects can use these descriptive profiles to statistically control for differences in case-mix among groups.

Data Collection

The caliber of an economic evaluation is heavily dependent on the rigor of the research methodology employed by investigators and the quality of the information upon which analyses are conducted. The information collected for the purpose of the evaluation should be valid and reliable.

Measurement Process

Where possible, evaluators should be trained in administering and scoring assessment instruments, randomly assigned to participants, and blinded as to the type of intervention that service recipients received. These methods are used to optimize measurement accuracy and minimize bias. Otherwise, evaluators who hold beliefs about the superiority or inferiority of an intervention can consciously or unconsciously influence the data collected through the measurement process. Therefore, these strategies help to ensure that measured differences among service recipients stem from the intervention rather than measurement bias.

Measuring Outcomes

The method by which health and economic outcomes are measured affects data quality, as measurement instruments vary in their accuracy (i.e., validity and reliability). Therefore, it is imperative that investigators determine and report the psychometric properties of any assessment tools that are used. Changes that are made in the standardized administration of these tools, however slight, may alter these properties and should be avoided or reported. Chapter 6 provides a more thorough discussion regarding the different types of validity and reliability. At a minimum, all assessment tools should be selected on the basis of their content validity. Assessments that are used to detect change over time should demonstrate adequate content and construct validity as well as interrater and test-retest reliability and responsiveness.

Measuring Costs

Most payers and service providers are interested in the average cost of services per client. However, the average or mean cost can be influenced by very high- or low-cost clients (also termed *outliers*). For example, imagine that the last 50 persons who received services from a specific health care program cost a payer organization an average of $100. The range of costs was from $75 to $125 per episode of care per person. During the past week, one client participated in the program for an unusually long period of time, and the cost to the payer was $250. When conducting a cost assessment, it was determined that if this charge was included in the analysis the average cost per episode would increase to $103.

Investigators must determine whether to include outliers when calculating average costs. This decision should be made by considering the frequency with which services are delivered to these persons and future opportunities to recover or negotiate alterations in charges to accommodate for the unique needs of this clientele. Statistically, service providers can use average costs to negotiate remuneration rates and diversify the risk of financing the cost of infrequent, high-cost clienteles through the delivery of services to infrequent, low-cost clienteles. This risk diversification is only achieved through the delivery of high volume services over extended periods of time.

One alternative to reporting average costs is to provide median and range values. The median is also a measure of central tendency, but this value is not sensitive to outliers. The median cost of a health service is the cost above and below which half the cases fall; therefore, the median is equal to the 50th percentile. If there is an even number of cases in a sample the median is the average of the two middle cases when costs per case are sorted in ascending or descending order.

The most difficult resource contributions to measure and value are those that are consumed in the distant future. In general, people have a preference for paying money in the future rather than today and tend to place a different value on a dollar earned or paid today versus a dollar earned or paid in the future. For example, some prefer to make payments in the future when the money that would be used for this purpose could be invested and accrue interest until the payment due date. This concept, which is referred to as the *time value of money*, should be incorporated into cost-effectiveness analyses that involve long periods of time. For example, Boyle, Torrance, Sinclair, and Horwood (1983) considered the time value of money when conducting an economic evaluation on the use of intensive care units for very-low-birth-weight infants. These investigators considered the effect of this intervention on future health and social service costs such as special education and supportive living arrangements.

Another principle in support of this preference for paying money in the future is that there tends to be more uncertainty regarding benefits that may accrue in the distant future or who might reap these rewards. For example, if there is uncertainty regarding the magnitude of future benefits (e.g., less health service use), service agencies might prefer to defer or avoid expenditures (e.g., investment in a health prevention program), particularly when other health service organizations might reap the benefits of these rewards (e.g., financial savings related to less health service use).

The Public Health Service's Panel on Cost-Effectiveness in Health and Medicine recommended that cost analyses be conducted using constant dollars. In other words, costs should not be increased each year to account for inflation. In addition, the time value of money concept should be considered when valuing any costs or effects that accrue in future time periods (Weinstein, Siegel, Gold, Kamlet, & Russell, 1996). The rationale for considering the time value of money is that the persons who use economic evaluations to compare services may place a different value on health benefits and costs that accrue in the near versus distant future. Readers who are interested in the valuation of financial costs and economic benefits that accrue over long-term time horizons should review the articles by Krahn and Gafni (1993) and Lipscomb, Weinstein, and Torrance (1996). The future cost of providing services to persons who live longer secondary to an intervention provided today is a contentious issue in the economic evaluation literature. Readers who are interested in this issue should review the article by Meltzer (1997).

Data Analysis

Investigators should clearly document the statistical methods used to examine the data, and the hypotheses tested in the analysis process should be determined by the research question that was used to focus the scope of the evaluation. In general, these analyses should begin with a profile of all variables using descriptive statistics.

Inferential statistical tests such as the chi-square, Wilcoxon signed ranks test, and Student's *t*-test should be used to test for significant baseline differences between the sample of persons used in the evaluation and all service recipients (i.e., representativeness) and baseline characteristics of persons in the services being compared (i.e., case-mix differences). Multivariate models can then be employed to test for significant associations between independent and dependent variables, after controlling for any case-mix or baseline differences between these groups. Investigators should demonstrate that they have used sample sizes that are sufficiently large enough to detect true differences between groups and test hypotheses regarding significant associations. Katz et al. (1995) wrote an excellent article regarding the use of statistics to assist rehabilitation practitioners in appraising and conducting clinical research.

Sensitivity Analyses

Good evaluations should include an assessment regarding the robustness of the findings. These assessments, termed *sensitivity analyses*, are required as investigators must make a number of judgments or assumptions throughout the course of an analysis. A sensitivity analysis presents the range of possible values resulting from variations of a critical judgment (Drummond et al., 1997). If the analysis creates insignificant variation in the results, decision makers should have confidence in the results. However, if the sensitivity analysis reveals substantial variability in costs or outcomes, greater accuracy is needed in the measurement of critical variables. The book by Drummond et al. (1997) outlines the steps to take when conducting this type of assessment.

Rizzo et al. (1996) conducted a sensitivity analysis when they conducted a cost-effectiveness and cost-benefit analysis to determine the relative value of two approaches to preventing falls in the elderly. They conducted the analysis using mean and median costs and widely different assumptions regarding the financial figures used to calculate intervention costs and economic benefits. Ruchlin and Morris (1981) also conducted a sensitivity analysis when they conducted a cost-benefit analysis to determine the net financial effect of offering an emergency alarm and response system to seniors who live in the community. These investigators identified different target populations including persons who were socially isolated and severely functionally impaired, not socially isolated and severely functionally impaired, and socially isolated but moderately functionally impaired or medically vulnerable. These three groups were selected to determine whether the results were dependent on the clientele served.

Interpretation of Findings

Investigators who conduct evaluations should provide decision makers with information to make judgments regarding the internal and external validity of the assessment. The methods used to recruit persons, measure costs and outcomes, analyze data, and interpret results should be explicit and any assumptions declared and justified. The robustness of conclusions should be tested as part of a good sensitivity analysis. All studies are hampered by limitations, but a final report that includes a description of these shortcomings will ultimately help decision makers to weigh the merits of the evaluation and, thereby, make judgments based on evidence and reason.

Good studies document and describe sources of bias, contamination, and noncompliance (Hoffman et al., 1994). The primary sources of bias include selection, assignment, and measurement. Contamination occurs in comparative studies when persons receive therapeutic interventions, intentionally or inadvertently, in addition to or instead of the service that is being evaluated. For example, when service recipients receive adjunct therapies (e.g., physical therapy) in addition to the service being evaluated (e.g., occupational therapy) it is difficult to discern which intervention is responsible for helping these persons to attain certain outcomes. The situation becomes more complex when these supplemental services are provided by other care givers or are not available to all persons included in the evaluation. Noncompliance also influences the results of an evaluation, as an intervention cannot be deemed to be effective if it is not received and the true effect of the intended intervention is difficult to discern (Shekelle, 1994). Therefore, the level of compliance with intervention protocols should be monitored and documented. Compliance may be enhanced by positively reinforcing participation, using diaries, and scheduling frequent follow-up appointments (Hoffman et al, 1994).

Summary

This chapter outlines a series of issues to consider when appraising or implementing an economic evaluation and builds on other conceptual and technical topics highlighted throughout the book. All good evaluations begin with a clear and explicit research question that focuses the scope of the project and a research design that maximizes the internal validity of the assessment. The health services being compared as well as the service recipients who participate in the evaluation should be described in sufficient detail that readers of the final report thoroughly understand the programs. All of the relevant costs and outcomes should be identified, and the most important of these variables should be included in the analysis. The methods by which persons were recruited for inclusion in the evaluation must be specified, and any strategy used to assign persons to services must be declared. Investigators should indicate when and how outcomes are measured and provide a brief summary regarding the psychometric soundness of the assessment tools used to measure these concepts. The source and quality of costing information are also important to declare. Investigators should account for attrition; identify sources of bias, contamination, and noncompliance; and discuss the limitations of the evaluation.

The final report provides decision makers with information regarding the relative value of service alternatives. Decisions that are based on available evidence are far superior to those based solely on instinct or intuition, particularly when the well-being of persons and large resources are at stake. The strategies and tips provided in this chapter should help current and future investigators to develop a basic understanding of the process by which good economic evaluations are designed and implemented. The Learning Resources section of this chapter as well as Appendix B offer references to those who wish to continue to develop their understanding of more complex methodological topics. ❖

Practice Exercises

Refer to Appendix D for responses to all questions.

1. You have obtained a copy of a clinical effectiveness study conducted by Law et al. (1997). The purpose of the study was to assess the effect of intensive neurodevelopmental treatment (i.e., twice weekly for 45 min for 4 months) and casting versus regular occupational therapy (i.e., once weekly for 45 min for 4 months) on hand function among children with cerebral palsy. This study incorporated a rigorous methodological design (i.e., randomized crossover design) to evaluate the effectiveness of these service alternatives.

   a. Why would you judge this study to be rigorous?

   b. What source(s) of bias may place limitations on the external validity of the findings?

2. The Practice Exercises in chapter 7 required that you conduct an assessment to compute the full cost of delivering intensive neurodevelopmental treatment versus a regular occupational therapy program. Notice from the example cost estimates provided in Appendix D Tables 13 and 14 that a large proportion of the full cost of these interventions was associated with institutional overhead. The accounting department has indicated that these indirect costs are only estimates and that the true cost of this resource may range between $30/hr and $45/hr. Conduct a sensitivity analysis to calculate the range within which the true cost of these services may be found.

References

Boyle, M. H., Torrance, G. W., Sinclair, J. C., & Horwood, S. P. (1983). Economic evaluation of neonatal intensive care of very-low-birth-weight infants. *New England Journal of Medicine, 308,* 1330–1337.

Campbell, D. T., & Stanley, J. C. (1966). *Experimental and quasi-experimental designs for research.* Skokie, IL: Rand McNally.

Drummond, M. F., O'Brien, B. J., Stoddart, G. L., & Torrance, G. (1997). *Methods for the economic evaluation of health care programmes* (2nd ed.). Oxford, UK: Oxford University Press.

Ellek, D. (1996). Policy implications of outcomes research. *American Journal of Occupational Therapy, 50,* 886–889.

Hoffman, R. M., Turner, J. A., Cherkin, D. C., Deyo, R. A., & Herron, L. D. (1994). Therapeutic trials for low back pain. *Spine. 19,* 18S, 2068S–2075S.

Johnston, M. V., & Miller, L. S. (1986). Cost-effectiveness of the Medicare three-hour regulation: Physical plus occupational therapy. *Archives of Physical Medicine and Rehabilitation, 67,* 581–585.

Katz, R. T., Campagnolo, D. I., Goldberg, G., Parker, J. C., Pine, Z. M., & Whyte, J. (1995). Critical evaluation of clinical research. *American Journal of Physical Medicine and Rehabilitation, 76,* 82–93.

Krahn, M., & Gafni, A. (1993). Discounting in the economic evaluation of health care interventions. *Medical Care, 31*, 403–418.

Law, M., Russell, D., Pollock, N. Rosenbaum, P., Walter, S., & King, G. (1997). A comparison of intensive neurodevelopmental therapy plus casting and a regular occupational therapy program for children with cerebral palsy. *Developmental Medicine and Child Neurology, 39*, 664–670.

Lipscomb, J., Weinstein, M. C., & Torrance, G. W. (1996). Time preference. In M. R. Gold, J. E. Siegel, L. B. Russell, & M. C. Weinstein (Eds.), *Cost-effectiveness in health and medicine* (pp. 214–246). New York: Oxford University Press.

Meltzer, D. (1997). Accounting for future costs in medical cost-effectiveness analysis. *Journal of Health Economics, 16*(1), 33–64.

Rich, M. W., Bechham, V., Wittenberg, C., Leven, C., Freedland, K. E., & Carney, R. M. (1995). A multidisciplinary intervention to prevent the readmission of elderly patients with congestive heart failure. *New England Journal of Medicine, 333*, 1190–1195.

Rizzo, J. A., Baker, D. I., McAvay, G., & Tinetti, M. E. (1996). The cost-effectiveness of a multifactorial targeted prevention program for falls among community elderly persons. *Medical Care, 34*, 954–969.

Ruchlin, H. S., & Morris, J. N. (1981). Cost-benefit analysis of an emergency alarm and response system: A case study of a long-term care program. *Health Services Research, 16*, 65–80.

Shekelle, P. G., Andersson, G., Bombardier, C., Cherkin, D., Deyo, R., Keeler, R., Lee, C., Liang, M., Lipscomb, B., Spratt, K., & Weinstein, J. (1994). A brief introduction to the critical reading of the clinical literature. *Spine, 19*, 18S, 2028S–2031S.

Shortell, S. M., & Richardson, W. C. (1978). *Health program evaluation*. St. Louis, MO: Mosby.

Torrance, G. W., Siegel, J. E., & Luce, B. R. (1996). Framing and designing the cost-effectiveness analysis. In M. R. Gold, J. E. Siegel, L. B. Russell, & M. C. Weinstein (Eds.), *Cost-effectiveness in health and medicine* (pp. 54–81). New York: Oxford University Press.

Weinstein, M. C., Siegel, J. E., Gold, M., Kamlet, M. S., & Russell, L. B. (1996). Recommendations of the Panel on Cost-Effectiveness in Health and Medicine. *Journal of the American Medical Association, 276*, 1253–1258.

Learning Resources

Research Designs

Campbell, D. T., & Stanley, J. C. (1966). *Experimental and quasi-experimental designs for research*. Skokie, IL: Rand McNally.

Cook, T. D., & Campbell, D. T. (1979). *Quasi-experimentation: Design and analysis issues for field settings*. Boston: Houghton Mifflin.

Katz, R. T., Campagnolo, D. I., Goldberg, G., Parker, J. C., Pine, Z. M., & Whyte, J. (1995). Critical evaluation of clinical research. *American Journal of Physical Medicine and Rehabilitation, 76*, 82–93.

Larson, E. B., (1993). Randomized clinical trials in single patients during a two-year period. *Journal of the American Medical Association, 270*, 2708–2712.

Ottenbacher, K. J. (1991). Clinically relevant designs for rehabilitation research: The ideographic model. *American Journal of Physical Medicine and Rehabilitation, 70*, Supplement, S144–150.

Economic Evaluation

Drummond, M. F., O'Brien, B. J., Stoddart, G. L,. & Torrance, G. (1997). *Methods for the economic evaluation of health care programmes* (2nd ed.). Oxford, UK: Oxford University Press.

Weinstein, M. C., Siegel, J. E., Gold, M. R., Kamlet, M. S., & Russell. L. B. (1996). Recommendations of the Panel of Cost-Effectiveness in Health and Medicine. *Journal of the American Medical Association, 276*, 15, 1253–1258.

Risk Adjustment

Iezzoni, L. I. (1995). Risk adjustment for medical effectiveness research: An overview of conceptual and methodology considerations. *Journal of Investigative Medicine, 43*, 136–150.

Iezzoni, L. I. (1997). *Risk adjustment for measuring healthcare outcomes*. Chicago: Health Administration Press.

Rochon, P. A., Katz, J. N., Morrow, L. A., McGlinachey-Berroth, R., Ahlquist, M. M., Sarkarati, M., & Minaker, K. L. (1996). Comorbid illness is associated with survival and length of hospital stay of patients with chronic disability: A prospective comparison of three comorbidity indices. *Medical Care, 34*, 1093–1101.

Segal, M. E., & Whyte, J. (1997). Modeling case mix adjustment of stroke rehabilitation outcomes. *American Journal of Physical Medicine and Rehabilitation, 76*, 154–161.

Section III

Communicating the Value of Clinical Services

9

Demonstrating Results: Planning a Communication Strategy

Outcome results [that are] presented in a concise, timely, understandable, and relevant manner can become a powerful management tool to assist in assessing quality, modifying programs, improving care for individuals clients, ... determining appropriateness of patient classification and payment systems, planning for future program development, marketing, and negotiating managed care contracts. (Forer, 1996, p. 9)

Learning Objectives

- Describe four steps to follow when designing a strategy to communicate the results of an evaluation.
- Identify characteristics of a target audience that may influence their information needs and preferences.
- List the type of information that is typically included in a full report or structured abstract.

After completing an analysis of the costs and outcomes of a health service, the next task is to share the results with a target audience in the most cost-effective manner. Communicating the results of an evaluation is one of the most important mechanisms that can be used to demonstrate the value of a health service, intervention, program, or product. Results that are presented in a succinct, timely, and relevant manner can have a powerful influence on the decision-making process of target audiences. Information that is ambiguous or presented in a haphazard manner may not instill confidence in the findings, results, or conclusions.

A clear and thorough presentation of results will help to avoid incomplete or incorrect communications. Incomplete messages may leave the audience with unanswered questions, whereas incorrect messages may result in persons drawing inaccurate conclusions. Unfortunately, casual mistakes can have quite an effect. "Since correction is more difficult once a message has been delivered, it's important to try to avoid misinterpretations beforehand" (Northey, 1990, p. 15). Therefore, taking the time and effort to design and implement a strategy to share the results of an evaluation will help ensure that the presentation will have the effect that was intended. Presenting results in a succinct, timely, and relevant manner requires planning and a substantial amount of time, effort, and forethought.

There are basically four steps to follow when designing a communication strategy. Step 1 involves determining the characteristics of the target audience, particularly information needs and preferences. Step 2 involves determining the type and scope of information that will be contained in the message. Step 3 involves selecting a mode or method of communication that most closely matches the learning styles as well as the needs and preferences of persons in the target audience and is appropriately matched to the type of information communicated. Step 4 entails soliciting and responding to feedback from stakeholder groups.

Step 1: Determining the Characteristics of the Target Audience

The first step in designing a successful communication strategy is to assess the characteristics of persons who will be the recipients of the evaluation results. The method of communication and the contents of the message should be structured to be sensitive to the learning styles and information needs of these persons. Presentations that address the information needs and preferences of persons in a target group should be less costly and more effective than communication strategies that attempt to meet the needs of all audiences. For example, providing evaluative results to mid-level managers in a timely fashion and in a format that they can use to communicate with their superiors will have more of an effect than either providing concise documentation too late or presenting results in a format that requires extensive revisions before it can be reused. This approach to profiling target audiences is used by successful businesses and organizations to advertise and market products and services.

Communication strategies should be responsive to the learning styles of persons in the target audience. Although there is a range of different approaches to learning, the most common include auditory, visual, kinesthetic, or a combination of these three. The auditory learner may benefit from a verbal presentation, whereas the visual learner may appreciate presentations that are supplemented with written materials such as slides, brochures, or pamphlets. Some visual learners may prefer results that are written in text format, whereas others will favor graphic illustrations such as tables and figures. The kinesthetic learner may want to tour the program's facilities and talk directly with service providers and clientele. When the learning styles of persons in the target audience are difficult to ascertain, a communication scheme that simultaneously addresses more than one style may be appropriate.

The information needs and preferences of persons in the target audience may be influenced by characteristics such as their level of knowledge, concern, or vested interest in the services; their roles or responsibilities with respect to decision-making; their attitudes and past experiences with service evaluations; and the political, social, and economic context of the evaluation. It is important to consider the effect or influence of these characteristics on persons in the target audience and any implications this may have for the message that will be communicated as well as the format by which information will be disseminated. In addition to understanding the characteristics of the primary audience of the evaluation report, it may be appropriate to profile persons in a secondary audience, as many health care organizations typically require that a group be involved in decision-making. The communication strategy should focus on the initial transfer of information to the primary target audience.

Another issue that is intimately tied to the successful transmittal and receipt of information between persons and within an organization is the use or misuse of time. People place different value on their time, and everyone makes choices as to how to allocate the time they spend at work among various activities. Investigators who have a vested interest in an evaluation often value their assessment and want to spend a substantial amount of time communicating their results. The amount of time spent communicating results to the target audience should be primarily driven by the time restraints of these persons. Presenters must be respectful of the time they spend with others. Investigators should determine the amount of time that is available to share results before planning a communication strategy.

By conducting an evaluation that considers the costs and outcomes of a clinical service, investigators have already taken the first step to meeting a wide range of information needs of various persons. These audiences will now be aware of both the resource requirements and the expected effect of the service. This type of information is required to demonstrate the value of a service and is more informative than evaluations that simply offer insight regarding the effectiveness of intervention. By understanding the information needs of persons in the target audience, investigators will be best prepared to design a successful communication strategy.

Step 2: Determining the Type and Scope of Information in the Message

After profiling the information needs and preferences of the target audience, presenters should carefully consider the type and scope of information that will be contained in the message. In general, messages that are simple, straightforward, specific, and thorough will have the most effect on decision makers. Simplicity ensures that all persons receive the message in a timely fashion and correctly understand the content. Messages that are straightforward and specific provide just enough detail so that all of the information needs of persons in the audience are met. Thorough reports ensure that there are no unanswered questions.

Drummond, O'Brien, Stoddart, and Torrance (1997) provided a checklist to assist in appraising economic evaluations; this list can be used to ensure that the results of an assessment are presented in a thorough and informative manner. In general, these authors suggested that a sound evaluation should state a well-defined research question, provide a comprehensive description of service alternatives, establish the effectiveness of the service, identify and accurately measure all of the important and relevant costs, offer an incremental analysis, adjust for differential timing, and account for uncertainty in estimates. Although the majority of the chapters in this book focus on the first five items on this list, chapter 8 addresses the issues of differential timing and accounting for uncertainty in estimates.

The Panel on Cost-Effectiveness in Health and Medicine, which was established by the Public Health Service in the United States, offers recommendations to investigators who will be reporting the process and outcome of a cost-effectiveness analysis (Siegel, Weinstein, Russell, & Gold, 1996). Although a full checklist is provided on page 1340 of Siegel et al. (1996), these recommendations basically suggest that a full report contain information on the

- background of the investigation and include a description of the target services, the context of the intervention, the boundaries and time horizon of the evaluation, as well as a statement of the analysis perspective;
- methods used to conduct the investigation including a description of the sources and quality of data, the costs and outcomes included in the evaluation, and strategies used to estimate effectiveness, resource use, and unit costs;
- results of the evaluation including total and incremental costs and effectiveness and information obtained from sensitivity analysis; and
- conclusions reached by investigators including a summary of assumptions, findings, limitations, implications, and a statement of relevance.

Full reports contain formal documentation of the process and outcome of an evaluation and offer the reader the opportunity to adequately assess the internal and external validity of the assessment. *Internal validity* refers to the extent to which costs and outcomes are attributable to the service rather than competing explanations. *External validity* refers to the extent to which findings can be generalized to similar persons or comparable services. Internal validity is more important than external validity because there must be certainty that the observed costs and outcomes are attributable to a service before results can be generalized to similar situations (Shortell & Richardson, 1978).

Step 3: The Mode of Communication

There are numerous methods by which messages can be transmitted from the messenger to the receiver. However, the most successful presentations use a mode of communication that closely matches the learning styles, needs, and preferences of the target audience and is appropriately matched to the type of information communicated. For example, the mode of communication that closely matches the needs of the auditory learner is a verbal presentation. However, it would be inappropriate to provide detailed costing information to this audience without visual aids such as financial statements or graphic illustrations. In this context it may be appropriate to supplement a verbal presentation with written documentation or visual aids.

More often than not, the audience will consist of a group of persons who have different learning styles. In addition, many will eventually pass information on to others or try to recall details of the evaluation at a later date. Therefore, it is advisable to supplement all presentations with written documentation. Investigators must determine how much documentation to provide, what information will be shared, and what format written reports will take.

Written material has staying power as it provides a permanent record of information. This mode of communication helps persons to reread information to clarify and enrich their thoughts about the evaluation or to share information with other interested persons. Printed documents also have traveling power, as clearly written ideas that meet the information needs of a range of persons will travel quickly to decision makers. These documents often take a voyage through a health service organization and ultimately influence current and future actions. Written documents need only an adequate filing system to stay alive, whereas verbal presentations must rely on memory. The staying and traveling power of written materials (e.g., reports) has an enormous influence over people (Northey, 1990).

The format, style, layout, tone, and content of written documents should be structured to meet the information needs and preferences of persons in the target audience. For example, persons who have a vested interest in an evaluation may value a formal report whereas others may be more interested in summary documentation. In addition, some may be interested in the methodological strategy used by investigators, whereas others may simply want a synopsis of the conclusions.

It is advisable to structure formal reports to meet the current and potential future needs of decision makers who will be privy to the contents of the report. Northey (1990) recommended that formal reports contain a summary or synopsis, an introduction, a discussion of findings, recommendations, and conclusions. The synopsis of a formal report is often referred to as an *executive summary*. These summaries provide a one-page synopsis of the purpose, methods, issues, and conclusions and may be the only section read by some persons. The introductory section should include a statement of purpose, background, scope, and methods. Investigators should provide a discussion of the findings and offer an objective account of the facts upon which the conclusions and recommendations are based. Recommendations should be listed and bulleting can be used for ease of reference; a brief paragraph can be provided next to each recommendation to justify the statement.

In addition, it may be appropriate to structure lengthy reports to satisfy the needs of those who will spend 2, 5, or 10 or more minutes reading this document. For example, a person who spends 2 minutes reviewing an evaluation report would benefit from an executive summary or structured abstract. This narrative is typically placed at the beginning of a full report. Structured abstracts have been standardized by editors of peer-reviewed journals over the past few years in an attempt to make these synopses more informative and clinically useful. Table 10 summarizes the type of information that should be included in a structured abstract and describes the relevance of each area to the presentation of the results of an evaluation. These summaries can be written with section headings or in paragraph form. Executive summaries or structured abstracts can be published in brochures, pamphlets, and Internet web sites with accompanying illustrations such as tables, charts, and graphs for persons who wish to spend 2 to 5 minutes reviewing the results of an evaluation. It is advisable to include the name and phone number of the principal investigator on the executive summary or structured abstract, as this document is often photocopied for dissemination.

Persons who wish to spend approximately 5 minutes reviewing or rereading a full report might benefit from a table of contents that quickly guides the reader to information on the following topics: the purpose of the analysis; details regarding primary and alternative services; the social, demographic, and clinical profile of the persons served and evaluated; strategies used to identify, measure, and value the costs and outcomes; the methods used to collect and analyze data; significant findings; and recommendations. Important sentences within the body of the text as well as significant findings and recommendations can be underscored or highlighted in bold to help these "5-minutes" readers to quickly review or locate important statements.

One mechanism that can be used to disseminate the results of an investigation is publication of the full report in a peer-reviewed journal. Appendix C provides a list of evaluations that have been published in the literature. There are two advantages to this approach: (a) results are circulated to a wide audience, and (b) the evaluation may be deemed to have more credibility after it has passed the peer-review process. A manuscript

Table 10
Presenting the Results of a Service Evaluation

Type of Information	Examples
Statement of the purpose or objective(s)	Type of evaluation, service(s) evaluated, target population, perspective of the analysis, costs, and outcomes considered
Design of the evaluation	Posttest or one-shot case study, one group pretest–posttest design, static group comparison, nonequivalent control group, and repeated measures
Methods used to determine effectiveness and cost	Observational or experimental design; sources of bias and methods used to minimize (e.g., single-blind); measurement, instrumentation, and methods used to ensure accuracy (e.g., training and assessment of evaluators)
Service setting or context	Inpatient, outpatient, institution-based, home-based, and community-based
Patients and participants	Sampling strategy including the selection and allocation of participants to groups using random, stratified, or matched approaches; inclusion or exclusion criteria; size, characteristics, and profile of participants including age, gender, level of acuity, severity of illness, and comorbid conditions
Description of service, intervention, program, or product being evaluated	Activities, frequency, intensity, duration, and background of clinical staff members
Main data sources and outcome measures	Surveys, questionnaires, clinical data, and administrative databases; scope of outcomes measured and instruments used
Results and conclusions	Summarize findings using text and illustrations such as tables, figures, charts, and graphs

that is submitted to a professional journal for publication is reviewed and appraised by a small group of peers or experts who provide feedback to the editor and author. This peer-review and editorial process requires that investigators conduct rigorous evaluations; ensures that findings are presented in a clear, concise, and thorough manner; and affirms that the author has meet the information needs of a wide audience. After the manuscript is printed in a journal, most publishers offer authors the opportunity to purchase reprints of the article at a nominal fee. This reprint can be disseminated to persons in the target audience who value this reporting format.

Designing successful written reports for a defined, target audience requires considerable effort and foresight. Consumers of written information will not be provided with the opportunity to clarify issues or misconceptions. Therefore, the style, layout, tone, and content of the report should be determined after an assessment is conducted to determine the learning styles and information needs of the target audience. Box 9 provides an example of a communication strategy that was designed to meet the needs of a specific audience.

Tables, figures, and graphic illustrations aid in summarizing, clarifying, or highlighting the most important and relevant findings. Although there are many different types of graphs, the selection of which illustration to use will depend on the purpose of the assessment, the context of the evaluation, and the characteristics of the target audience. The most popu-

---

Box 9
Example Communication Strategy

Imagine that you have been invited to summarize your evaluation to an audience that primarily includes mid-level managers in a health care organization. This group meets regularly to collaboratively plan their organizational marketing strategy. You have determined that their meetings are highly structured, last for 60 minutes, and follow a strict agenda due to the large number of issues that must be addressed. Clinical practitioners and persons from the finance department both attend the session.

One communication strategy that might be appropriate given this limited information regarding the target audience would be to provide a 10-minute verbal presentation with visual aids, give a full report to the committee chairperson before the meeting, and offer a structured abstract to each committee member before the presentation. Chapter 10 can be used to assist investigators in designing these visual aids. This communication strategy might be quite different if your target audience included payers or consumers. Before the meeting it may be appropriate to review office supply catalogues to obtain products that would enhance the quality of the presentation. In addition, it may even be worthwhile to hire or consult with a person who specializes in the design and fabrication of professional presentations.

---

lar and useful graphs include the scatter plot, the line chart, the bar chart, and the box plot. The graph should be simple to understand and communicate an array of information. Each axis should be labeled and include the unit of measurement. Legends should be provided when necessary, and captions should be used sparingly. The title of each illustration should be informative and include the sample size. In addition, a brief notation describing the intervention and the type of measurement instrument used to assess outcomes may be appropriate to use. Effective graphs communicate a tremendous amount of information in a short period of time, but they take skill and time to create. Chapter 10 provides assistance in the design and fabrication of these visual aids.

Step 4: Soliciting and Responding to Feedback From Stakeholder Groups

Effective communication is a two-way interaction. It is important to seek and respond to feedback from different stakeholder groups during the planning and concluding stages of an evaluation to ensure that they understood the evaluation and its implications and have the opportunity to provide feedback. Positive and negative feedback may be directed toward the stated purpose of the evaluation, the validity and reliability of the study, the findings obtained and the recommendations made by investigators. In addition, these persons may provide valuable insight regarding the completeness and accuracy of an evaluation report before its use for decision-making.

Summary

Communicating the results of an evaluation is one of the most important mechanisms that can be used to demonstrate the value of a health service. Results that are presented in a succinct, timely, and relevant manner can have a powerful influence on the decision-making process. When designing a communication strategy, investigators should assess the characteristics of persons who will be the recipients of the evaluation results. The method used to communicate results and the contents of this message should be structured to be sensitive to their learning styles and information needs. By soliciting and responding to feedback from various stakeholder groups during the planning and concluding phases of an assessment, investigators are better able to ensure the completeness and accuracy of their evaluation. ❖

References

Drummond, M. F., O'Brien, B. J., Stoddart, G. L., & Torrance, G. (1997). *Methods for the economic evaluation of health care programmes* (2nd ed.). Oxford, UK: Oxford University Press.

Forer, S. (1996). *Outcome management and program evaluation made easy: A tool kit for occupational therapy practitioners*. Rockville, MD: American Occupational Therapy Association.

Northey, M. (1990). *Impact: A guide to business communication* (2nd ed.). Scarborough, Ontario: Prentice-Hall.

Shortell, S. M., & Richardson, W. C. (1978). *Health program evaluation*. St. Louis, MO: Mosby.

Siegal. J. E., Weinstein, M. C., Russel, L. B., & Gold, M. R. (1996). Recommendations for reporting cost-effectiveness analyses. *Journal of the American Medical Association, 276*, 16, 1339–1341.

Learning Resources

Ad Hoc Working Group for Clinical Appraisal of the Medical Literature. (1987). A proposal for more informative abstracts of clinical articles. *Annals of Internal Medicine, 106*, 598–604.

Burnett, R. E. (1990). *Technical communication* (2nd ed.). Belmont, CA: Wadsworth.

Siegal. J. E., Weinstein, M. C., Russel, L. B., & Gold, M. R. (1996). Recommendations for reporting cost-effectiveness analyses. *Journal of the American Medical Association, 276*, 16, 1339–1341.

Squires, B. P., Keith, R .G., & Meakins, J. L. (1992). Structure abstracts for clinical research manuscripts and review. *Canadian Journal of Surgery, 35*, 473–475.

10
Demonstrating Results: Designing Graphic Illustrations

Figures convey at a quick glance an overall pattern of results. They are especially useful in describing an interaction—or lack thereof—and nonlinear relationships. A well-prepared figure can also convey structural or pictorial concepts more efficiency than can text. (American Psychological Association, 1994, p. 141)

Learning Objectives

- Describe four types of graphs that can be used to summarize the results of an evaluation.
- Identify graphs that are most appropriate for describing individual or group-level data.
- Identify five items that should be included in any graphic illustration.

Graphic illustrations are one of a number of strategies that can be used to summarize and highlight the most important and relevant findings of an evaluation. This chapter will provide a brief description of different types of graphs, describe how these illustrations can be used to convey the results of an evaluation, and outline suggestions to guide the design of a graph to demonstrate the value of a specific health service.

Types of Graphic Illustrations

Planning and designing a graphic illustration requires that presenters reflect on how a figure could be used to provide information regarding the focus of the evaluation. Investigators must also consider the characteristics and information needs of the target audience and the message that will be communicated. The type of graph selected to illustrate the results of an evaluation will depend on these considerations. The most popular and useful graphs include the scatter plot, the line chart, the bar chart, and the box plot.

Scatter Plot

The scatter plot consists of a series of dots, each dot representing a single event or individual case. These graphs provide individual-level information about the relationship between two or more variables that have been measured for a particular case. For example, Figure 3 depicts the use of a scatter plot to illustrate the relationship between the amount of occupational therapy services received by a person (horizontal or x axis) and the amount that each person changed in terms of their independence in activities of daily living (vertical or y axis). Each dot represents the amount of service received and the amount of change in functional status achieved by one person. The person who experienced the most change during the course of this study, in terms of independence in activities of daily living, received 4.5 hr of service.

Scatter plots are often used by researchers to explore or visualize their data. This process helps investigators to quickly identify clusters of data points that might imply relationships, or extraordinarily large or small values that may reflect coding errors or represent individual cases that experienced extremely high or low costs and outcomes. Clusters of data points on a scatter plot imply relationships or correlations. For example, data points that cluster to form a line suggests that there is a strong, linear relationship between the variables measured. A positive, linear relationship implies that high or large values of one variable are associated with high or large values of a second variable. On a scatter plot this type of relationship is depicted by an upward sloped line, as illustrated in Figure 3. A negative, linear relationship implies that high or large values of one variable are associated with low or small values of a second variable. On a scatter plot this type of relationship is depicted by a downward sloped line.

A linear line has been fit to the data points on the scatter plot in Figure 3 to depict the strength (i.e., magnitude of the correlation or the slope of the line) and direction (i.e., positive correlation) of the relationship between service intensity and change in functional status. The upper and lower curvilinear lines represent the 95% confidence intervals around this correlation line. Many different computer software programs plot linear or curvilinear lines to evaluate these associations; the SPSS® statistical software program was used to generate the graph in Figure 3.

As the data points in Figure 3 do not cluster along a line, this chart suggests that there is a weak, positive, linear relationship (Pearson $r = 0.18$, $p = 0.23$) between the amount of time persons receive therapy (i.e., resource input) and changes in their functional status (i.e., health outcomes).[11] This

---

[11]The term *weak* is used to describe this relationship, as the correlation coefficient is not statistically significant and the data points in Figure 3 do not cluster around the regression or correlation line.

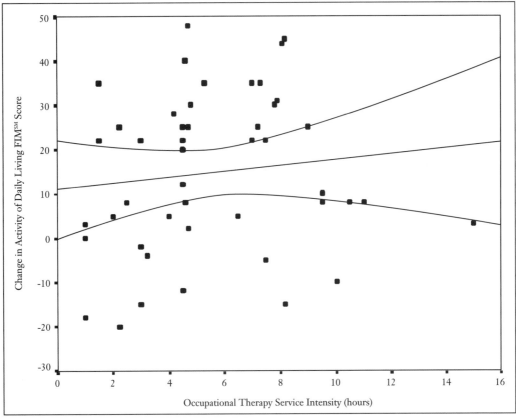

Figure 3. The relationship between service intensity and change in activities of daily living. *Note.* These persons (*n* = 45) received inpatient occupational therapy in an acute care hospital following a recent stroke. No adjustment has been made for initial severity of illness, length of stay, or the intensity of physical therapy services received. The relationship between occupational therapy service intensity and change in function is illustrated (Pearson *r* = 0.18, *p* = 0.23) as well as the 95% confidence interval for this correlation. The following subtests of the Functional Independence Measure[SM] (FIM[SM]) (Data Management Service, 1993) were used to measure activities of daily living: eating, grooming, bathing, dressing, toileting, bladder control, and bowel management.

graph was constructed after a pilot study was conducted before initiating a cost-effectiveness evaluation of providing inpatient, occupational therapy services to persons who had a recent stroke. After completing this pilot study, members of the project team met with clinical staff members to evaluate the results. It was determined that the sample of persons included in this initial analysis were too heterogeneous. Some of the patients had significant impairments initially, whereas other participants were mildly impaired. The clinical staff members suggested that this finding might explain the diversity of functional outcomes. Therefore, when the economic evaluation was implemented the investigators compiled information and constructed graphic illustrations for different subgroups of service clienteles (i.e., those with high- vs. low-initial functional status).

Data points on a scatter plot that represent extremely large or small values may suggest coding errors. For example, one of the data points on a scatter plot that looks at the relationship between age and performance on a standardized test may indicate that one person is 220 years old. In this context, the scatter plot would help investigators to quickly identify this type of coding error. Extreme or outlier data points may represent persons who have unusually high or low costs or outcomes. The person who received 15 hr of service intensity could be considered an outlier (Figure 3). This person received 5 hr more service than any other participant, and all other participants in this small sample received less than 10 hr of service. Outlier cases can dramatically influence calculations of central tendencies (e.g., mean) and measurements of association (e.g., correlation coefficients). For example, when the person who received 15 hr of service intensity was included in the sample of participants used to construct Figure 3, the correlation coefficient was not statistically significant (Pearson $r = 0.18$, $p = 0.23$). When this person was eliminated from the data the correlation coefficient increased and approached statistical significance (Pearson $r = 0.28$, $p = 0.07$). Therefore, once an outlier case is identified with a scatter plot, a decision regarding the inclusion or exclusion of this case in the analysis may be warranted. The factors that influence this decision are described in more detail in chapter 8.

A cluster of data points on a scatter plot may suggest that certain analyses be performed for different subgroups of service recipients. For example, if a scatter plot had two clusters of data points the investigators should review the characteristics of cases within each cluster to determine what features may be distinctly unique between the groups. If most of the persons in one cluster were female and most persons in the second cluster were male, it may be that the outcomes vary among service participants based on their gender.

Alternatively, the lack of clustering of data points on a scatter plot may suggest that analyses be performed with clinically significant subgroups of interest. Clinical experience and the research question guide investigators as to how the data can be organized and visualized to determine whether significant relationships exist once different clinical contexts or conditions are considered. For example, the investigators who found the results illustrated in Figure 3 might consider reconstructing their graph to determine whether the type and strength of the relationship between service intensity and changes in functional status vary by different diagnostic groups or the initial functional status of the client. The investigators who are faced with the data in Figure 3 may determine that there is a significant, positive, linear relationship between service intensity and changes in functional status but that this relationship only holds true among those patients whose initial functional performance ratings are very low. Alternatively, no such relationship may be evident among service recipients who have high functional performance ratings on initial assessment, as their opportunity to attain high scores regarding change in functional status is low. In this example, aggregating data across heterogeneous cases might have hidden statistically significant associations of clinical interest. Further analysis of the data would help investigators address these clinical issues. Some software programs use markers to identify cases that belong to different subgroups of interest (e.g., diagnostic categories) and to plot linear or curvilinear lines to evaluate relationships among different subgroups.

Line Chart

Line charts are also used to illustrate the relationship between two or more variables and these figures are particularly useful in portraying data over a period of time. Figure 4 provides an example of the use of a line chart to demonstrate the cumulative costs and incremental financial ben-

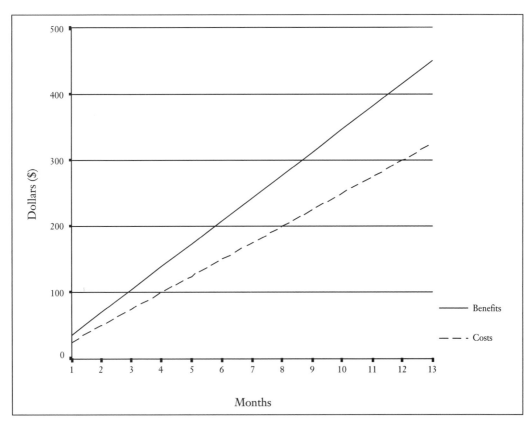

Figure 4. Cumulative average per person costs and incremental benefits of an emergency alarm and response system. *Note. n* = 139. The values used to create Figure 4 were taken from Ruchlin and Morris (1981).

efits that can accrue over time to persons who receive a specific health program. Different colored lines could be used to document more than one outcome, illustrate the costs and effects of services for different client populations, or compare the cost and outcome data for different services. A legend must always be incorporated into the graph to reference the characteristics of each line.

The data that was used to construct Figure 4 was derived from a cost-benefit analysis conducted by Ruchlin and Morris (1981). These investigators assessed the costs and economic outcomes of providing an emergency alarm and response system to seniors to help them to safely maintain their independence at home. The analysis was conducted from the societal perspective with a time horizon of 13 months; the comparison group was the delivery of "no service." The average cost per person per month for this type of intervention was $24.97. The economic outcomes that were identified, measured, and valued included direct savings from reduction in the use of institutional care; formal community services; and informal support services such as family members offering home making, and meal support. These financial savings averaged $34.58 per person/month. Intangible benefits such as feelings of enhanced personal security or reductions in the use of police or fire departments were not included in the analysis.

Analysis of Figure 4 suggests that the initial costs (i.e., $24.97) and economic outcomes (i.e., $34.58) of the service after the first month are initially similar, as the difference between these two figures was only $9.61. By the second month the total cumulative cost of the service (i.e., $24.97 for 2 months = $49.94) was lower than the accumulated benefits (i.e., $34.58 for 2 months = $69.16). The net financial effect of offering the intervention over the course of 2 months equals the distance between the two lines on the chart or $19.22 (i.e., $69.16 – $49.94). As each month passes, financial benefits exceed costs and the magnitude of this margin increased as time based. After 1 year, the cumulative, average cost of the service per recipient is approximately $320, and the cumulative, average benefit per recipient is approximately $450. The net financial effect per recipient over this 1-year period of time is a savings of $130. Notice that the area between the cost and benefit line in Figure 4 represents the net financial effect that accrues following implementation of the program over the course of 13 months.

In the situation described by Ruchlin and Morris (1981) the cost of the intervention always remained lower than the economic outcomes (i.e., financial benefits) of the intervention. This is typically not the case in health care, where the initial start-up cost or investment that is incurred to offer a service is often much larger than the initial financial benefits. However, over time financial benefits may accrue at a more rapid rate than growth in expenditures on resource contributions. Therefore, the data provided by Ruchlin and Morris was modified in Figure 5 to depict a hypothetical situation where costs initially exceed economic outcomes, but the financial benefits increase at a faster rate than expenditures over time. In this situation, a breakeven point can be clearly demonstrated with a line chart. This breakeven point (i.e., 7th month) represents the moment in time when costs are equal to benefits and after which benefits exceed costs. Time is always portrayed on the *x* axis of a line chart.

Bar Chart

The bar graph can be used to depict information at one point in history or to illustrate trends or changes over time. These figures portray information for categorical variables such as age groups (e.g., Figure 6), diagnostic conditions (e.g., Figure 7), or groups of persons who differ in their initial illness severity or who receive different service intensities. Alternatively, percentile ranks can also be used to categorize or cluster persons in the sample. Quartiles are often used to divide a distribution into four parts (i.e., 0–25

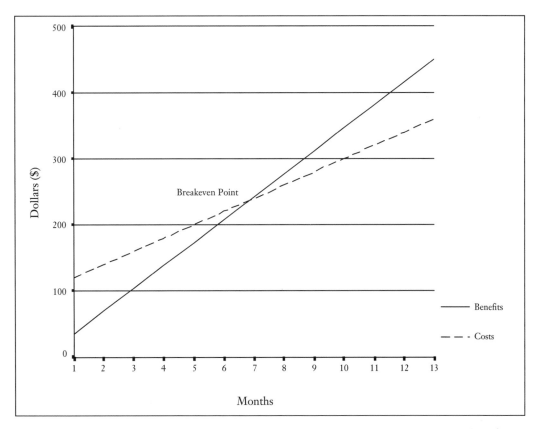

Figure 5. Line graph demonstrating breakeven point between intervention costs and benefits.

percentile, 26–50 percentile, 51–75 percentile, and 76–100 percentile), whereas a quintile can be used to divide a distribution into five equal parts (i.e., 0–20 percentile, etc.). When using a clustering approach to present data, the investigator should ensure that there are enough persons to adequately represent the typical performance of each group.

Although vertical bars are most commonly used, horizontal bars can enhance the visual effect of the graphic illustration. Bars can also be subdivided into categorizes to portray different characteristics of a group of persons. Figure 7 provides an example of how this strategy can be used to portray information regarding the average costs and changes in functional status of persons who are different ages. The values used to create this figure were derived from a cost-effectiveness and cost-utility analysis of joint replacement surgery conducted in Finland by Rissanen et al. (1997), who calculated the average cost per total knee replacement for service recipients who were less than 60 years of age and determined that the cost of

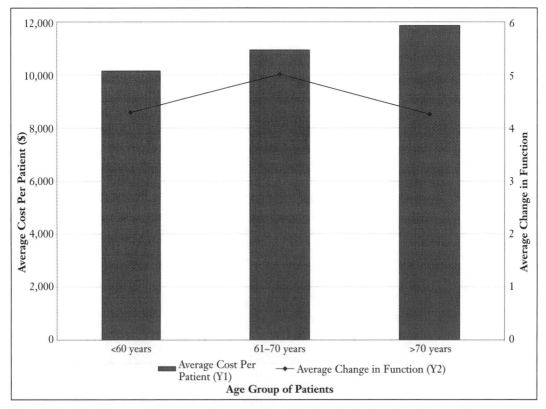

Figure 6. Total knee replacement: Average cost and change in functional status by age group. *Note. n* = 274. The values used to create this figure were taken from Rissanen et al. (1997). Functional status was measured with a 14-item scale of activities of daily living.

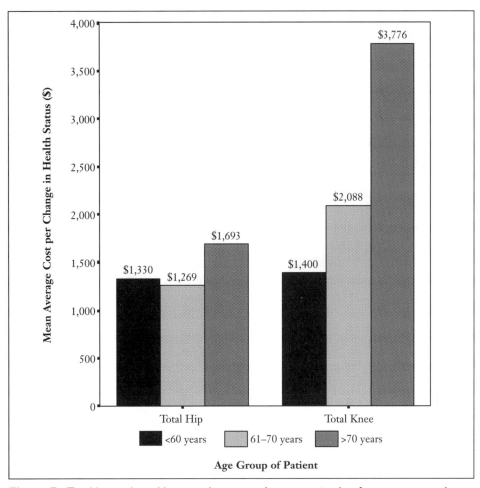

Figure 7. Total hip and total knee replacement: Average episode of care costs per change in health status. *Note. n* = 447. The values used to create this figure were taken from Rissanen et al. (1997). Health status was measured with a 15-dimension measure of health-related quality of life (Sintonen & Pekurinen, 1993).

this intervention was $10,146.[12] In addition, these persons experienced an average change in functional status of four units.[13] Patients who were 71 years of age or older experienced the same amount of change but cost an average of $11,860 per person. These investigators took the societal perspective when conducting the cost assessment and included the costs of hospital and social services as well as patients' out-of-pocket expenses.

[12]The study was conducted in Finland. The dollar figures shown here were calculated using the Finnish/United States exchange rate at the time of the evaluation.
[13]The effect of the intervention on a recipient's independence in activities of daily living was measured using a scale with 14 items.

Both *y* axes can be used in line and bar graphs to depict different variables and units of measurement. Figure 6 provides an example of this strategy. In this context, the left vertical axis is referred to as *y1*, which depicts the average cost of intervention per patient. The right axis is *y2*, which depicts the average change in functional status of persons who received a total knee replacement.

Rather than provide two *y* axes that simultaneously provide information on costs and outcomes (e.g., Figure 6), these variables can be consolidated into costs per unit of change in health and depicted on a single *y* axis. Figure 7 provides an example of this strategy. This bar chart illustrates the average episode of care and cost per unit of change in health status for different cohorts of patients. The value depicted on the *y* axis was calculated by dividing the average cost of an episode of care for patients in a specific cohort (e.g., persons < 60 years of age with a total hip replacement) by their average change in health status. Figure 7 suggests that it costs approximately $1,400 to improve the health status[14] of a young recipient of a total knee by one unit of health but cost $3,776 to achieve a similar improvement in the health status of an older recipient. In addition, whereas it cost $1,400 to improve the health status of a young recipient of a total knee by one unit of health, it cost approximately $1,330 to achieve a similar improvement in the health status of a person in the same age cohort who received a total hip replacement. The statement that it is more costly to attain improvements in health status among persons who receive a knee versus those who receive a hip replacement appears to be true irrespective of the age group.

Box Plot

The box plot displays group-level summary statistics and is appropriate to use to portray the distribution of specific characteristics as demonstrated in Figure 8. The thick, horizontal line drawn within the box represents the median or middle value of the distribution. The lower boundary of the box is the 25th percentile whereas the upper border represents the 75th percentile, therefore 50% of persons have values (e.g., change in functional status) that fall within the boundaries of the box. A vertical line is drawn above the box to represent the largest observed value that is not an outlier, whereas the vertical line drawn below the box depicts the smallest observed value that is not an outlier (Norusis, 1993).

Figure 8 provides an example of the use of the box plot to portray the distribution of change in functional status for a small group of stroke survivors who received rehabilitation services in an acute care hospital for

---

[14]This $1,400 reflects the cost per unit of health status. Rissanen et al. (1997) used a 15-dimension measure of health-related quality of life when they conducted this cost-utility analysis of hip and knee replacement surgery.

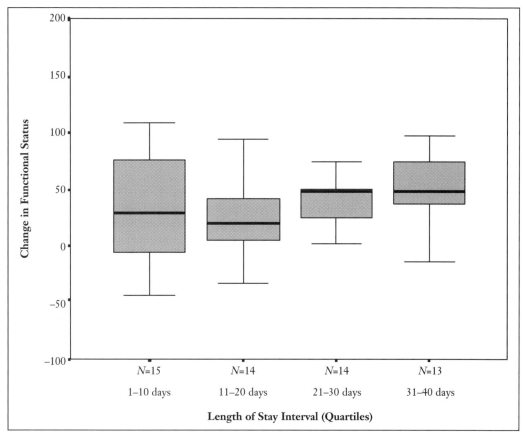

Figure 8. Stroke recovery in an acute care rehabilitation program: Average change in functional status by length of stay. *Note. n* = 56. Change in functional status was measured with the Functional Independence Measure[SM] (Data Management Service, 1993). Adapted from Table 3 "Cost-Benefit Analysis of Level II Fieldwork in Occupational Therapy" by L. D. Shalik, 1987, *American Journal of Occupational Therapy, 41,* p. 641. Copyright 1987 by the American Occupational Therapy Association. Adapted with permission.

different intervals of time. For example, the median change in functional status for those who stayed in the acute care rehabilitation program for 1 to 10 days was approximately 30 units of function.[15] This magnitude of change is approximately the same for those who stay 11 to 20 days. However, patients who received services longer (e.g., 21–40 days) attained a median change in function equivalent to approximately 50 units. In addition,

---

[15]Change in functional status was measured using the Functional Independence Measure[SM] (Data Management Service, 1993).

there appears to be more diversity in outcomes among those who stay for short periods of time than those who stayed longer. This is evident by the size of the box plot. Those who stay for shorter periods (e.g., 1–10 days) experience more variable outcomes (e.g., 25th percentile value of approximately –5; 75th percentile value of approximately 75) than persons who stay longer (e.g., length of stay of 21–30 days; 25th percentile value of 25; 75th percentile value of 50). It is important to note that the sample of persons included in this pilot study was small. The number of persons represented in each box plot has been specified on the figure.

Designing a Graphic Illustration

Although there are many different types of graphs, the selection of which figure to use will depend on the purpose of the evaluation, the context of the presentation, and the information needs of the target audience. Planning and designing a graphic illustration requires that presenters reflect on how a figure could be used to provide information regarding the focus of the evaluation. Investigators must also consider the characteristics of the target audience and the message that will be communicated. This message should be presented in a format that meets the information needs and requirements of the target audience. In essence, investigators should follow the same four steps described in chapter 9. Recall from this chapter that any strategy to communicate the results of an evaluation should involve a determination of the learning styles as well as information needs and preferences of the target audience, a determination of the type and scope of information that will be contained in the message, the selection of a mode of communication (i.e., type of graphic), and the solicitation of feedback from stakeholder groups.

The different graphs described and illustrated in this chapter simply offer some suggestions as to how economic evaluative data can be presented to depict the costs and outcomes of a health service. All graphic illustrations should be simple to understand and communicate an array of information. Each axis should be labeled and include the unit of measurement. Legends should be provided when necessary and captions should be used sparingly. The title of each illustration should be informative and include the sample size. In addition, a brief notation describing the intervention and the type of measurement instrument used to assess outcomes may be appropriate to include (see Figures 3 and 8).

To be most effective at demonstrating the results of an economic evaluation, graphs should include information on costs and outcomes simultaneously. This can be done by using the x and y axes to represent costs and outcomes (e.g., Figure 4), two lines on a line graph (e.g., Figure 5), two y axes (e.g., Figure 6), or ratios such as costs per change in health status (e.g., Figure 7). Typically, the independent variable is located on the horizontal or x axis of the graph, whereas the dependent variable is located on the vertical or y axis (American Psychological Association, 1994). In the context of economic evaluations, the intervention is the independent variable and both costs and outcomes are dependent variables. If graphs are used to illustrate the relationship between costs and outcomes, it is recommended that you select which variable should be placed on the x axis as this is the location on a graph that persons tend to reference first.

A decision must be made as to whether data will be displayed for various groups of persons or for each person in the study. The decision regarding the use of group or individual-level data will depend on the context of the evaluation and the type of results obtained. When group-level data are used, measures of central tendency (e.g., mean, median, mode) and variability (e.g., standard deviation) may be appropriate to incorporate into the figure. If it is important to illustrate the variability in costs and outcomes among different persons, it may be important to illustrate individual-level data with a scatter plot (e.g., Figure 3). This variability could be demonstrated at the group-level with the use of a box plot that simultaneously incorporates measures of central tendency and variability (e.g., Figure 8). If the cost or outcome of an intervention varies significantly by subgroup (e.g., age group, gender, diagnoses, initial severity of illness), the data may be more appropriately displayed by these categories (e.g., Figure 6).

Conclusion

Developing skills and proficiency in writing reports and designing effective graphics requires patience and a lot of practice. Start by becoming familiar with a software program that can be used to create graphs or work collaboratively with a person who has expertise and experience constructing these figures. Ask different persons to review draft illustrations to obtain feedback regarding how they are interpreted. Effective graphs communicate a tremendous amount of information in a short period of time but will take time to create. Don't give up too soon—the results are worth the effort. ❖

Practice Exercises

Assume that you completed a cost-benefit analysis of student fieldwork from the service delivery system perspective and obtained results similar to Shalik (1987). Recall from chapter 2 that this type of analysis requires that costs be related to the economic outcomes of a service. The results of this type of analysis can be presented as a sum of costs and benefits (i.e., net financial effect). When the value of the sum of costs and benefits is negative, costs are greater than benefits; when this quotient is positive, benefits are greater than costs (Zarnke, Levine, & O'Brien, 1997). Table 11 pro-

Table 11
The Net Financial Effect of Offering Level II Fieldwork by Week

Week of Fieldwork	Net Financial Effect in Dollars
1	–462.75
2	–175.31
3	156.35
4	107.59
5	595.75
6	212.68
7	664.93
8	686.00
9	858.06
10	617.11
11	720.87
12	731.25
13	144.67

Note. n = 156. Adapted from Table 3 "Cost-Benefit Analysis of Level II Fieldwork in Occupational Therapy," by L. D. Shalik, 1987, *American Journal of Occupational Therapy, 41*, p. 641. Copyright 1987 by the American Occupational Therapy Association. Adapted with permission.

vides a summary of Shalik's (1987) findings regarding the net financial effect to health care organizations of providing fieldwork experiences to students. Use these findings to design a graphic illustration. If you want assistance with this challenge, use the tips outlined below. Appendix D provides example graphic illustrations for this scenario.

1. Input the values from Table 11 in two columns in the spreadsheet program by Microsoft® called Excel.
2. Highlight these values and press the icon to activate ChartWizard. Drag the cursor to designate a space in the worksheet to insert a chart.
3. Confirm that your data is contained in the cells specified by ChartWizard. Press Next.
4. Select a chart type (e.g., Column). Press Next. This software program refers to graphics that incorporate vertical bars as Column Charts and those that have horizontal bars as Bar Charts.
5. Select a format for the chart. Press Next.

6. Identify which of the columns (i.e., 1st) contains information for the *x* axis (i.e., Week of Fieldwork). Press Next.
7. Do not add a Legend to the chart. Specify the title of the chart (i.e., Net Financial Effect of Offering Level II Fieldwork by Week [*n* = 156]), the *x* axis (i.e., Week of Fieldwork), and the *y* axis (i.e., Net Financial Effect [$]). Press Finish. This graph will embed itself into the spreadsheet and can be modified by double clicking on the chart and then each element in the graph. For example, use the mouse to double click on the chart, then double click on the title. Change the font size to enhance the visual presentation.

You should have produced a graphic illustration that is similar in appearance to Figure 10 in Appendix D. To enhance your skills at designing graphs attempt to reproduce Figure 11 from Appendix D with the numbers in Table 15. The cumulative effect by week of fieldwork to a health care organization can be determined by adding the net cost of offering education for each week of the experience. For example, the net financial effect of week 1 is an expenditure that equals $462.75 whereas the net effect at week 2 costs $638.06 (–$462.75 plus –$175.31). The cumulative financial effect of offering fieldwork over a 13-week period to the average student is equal to approximately $4,857. The graphic type used in Figure 11 is called *combination*. This illustration combines a bar and line chart to provide valuable information.

References

American Psychological Association. (1994). *Publication manual of the American Psychological Association* (4th ed.). Washington, DC: Author.

Data Management Service of the Uniform Data System for Medical Rehabilitation and the Center for Functional Assessment Research. State University of New York at Buffalo. (1993). *Guide for the Uniform Data Set for Medical Rehabilitation* (4th ed.). Buffalo, NY: Author.

Norusis, M. J., (1993). *SPSS® for Windows™ Base System User's Guide: Release 6.0.* Chicago: SPSS Incorporated.

Rissanen, P., Aro, P., Sintonen, H., Asikainen, K., Slätis, P., & Paavolainen, P. (1997). Costs and cost-effectiveness in hip and knee replacements: A prospective study. *International Journal of Technology Assessment in Health Care, 13*, 575–588.

Ruchlin, H. S., & Morris, J. N. (1981). Cost-benefit analysis of an emergency alarm and response system: A case study of a long-term care program. *Health Services Research, 16*, 65–80.

Shalik, L. D. (1987). Cost-benefit analysis of level II fieldwork in occupational therapy. *American Journal of Occupational Therapy, 41*, 638–645.

Sintonen, H., & Pekurinen, M. A. (1993). A fifteen-dimensional measure of health-related quality of life (15D) and its application. In S. R. Walker & R. M. Rosser

(Eds.), *Quality of life assessment: Key issues for the 1990s* (pp. 185–195). Dordrecht: Kluwer Academic Publishers.

Zarnke, K. B., Levine, M. A., & O'Brien, B. J. (1997). Cost benefit analyses in the health-care literature: Don't judge a study by its label. *Journal of Clinical Epidemiology, 50*, 813–822.

Learning Resource

Henry, G. T. (1997). *Creating effective graphs: Solutions for a variety of evaluation data.* Windsor, Canada: Jossey-Bass.

Appendix A

Popular Instruments in the Rehabilitation Outcomes Literature

Instruments That Measure Disability

Barthel Index (Mahoney & Barthel, 1965)

Chedoke-McMaster Stroke Assessment—Disability Inventory (Gowland et al., 1993)

Functional Independence Measure (FIM[SM])(Data Management Service, 1993)

Wee FIM® (Braun, Msall, & Granger, 1991)

Katz Index (Katz, Ford, Moskowitz, Jackson, & Jaffe, 1963)

Klein-Bell Activities of Daily Living (ADL) Scale (Klein & Bell, 1982)

Kohlman Evaluation of Living Skills (KELS) (Kohlman Thomson, 1992)

Patient Evaluation Conference System (PECS) (Harvey & Jellinek, 1981)

Pediatric Evaluation of Disability Inventory (PEDI) (Haley, Coster, Ludlow, Jaltiwanger, & Andrellos, 1992)

Instruments That Measure Handicap

Activity Pattern Indicators (Brown, Gordon, & Diller, 1984)

Canadian Occupational Performance Measure (Law et al., 1994)

Community Integration Questionnaire (Corrigan & Deming, 1995)

Craig Handicap Assessment and Reporting Technique (CHART) (Whiteneck, Clarlifue, Gerhart, Overholser, & Richardson, 1992).

London Handicap Scale (Harwood, Gompertz, & Ebramhims, 1994)

Safety Assessment of Function and the Environment for Rehabilitation (SAFER) (Oliver, Blathwayt, Brackley, & Tamaki, 1993)

The Functional Autonomy Measurement System (SMAF) (Hébert, Carrier, & Bilodeau, 1988)

Instruments That Measure Health-Related Quality of Life

Arthritis Impact Measurement Scales (Meenan, 1982)

Medical Outcomes Study 36-item Short-Form Health Survey (SF-36) (Ware & Sherbourne, 1992)

Medical Outcomes Study 12-Item Short-Form Health Survey (SF-12) (Ware, Kosinski, & Keller, 1996)

Sickness Impact Profile (Bergner, Bobbit, Carter, & Gilson, 1981)

Instruments That Measure Global Satisfaction

Client Satisfaction Questionnaire (CSQ-8) (Nguyen, Attkisson, & Stegner, 1983)

Evaluation Ranking Scale (Pascoe & Attkisson, 1983)

Visit-Specific Satisfaction Questionnaire (Ware & Hays, 1988)

Note. For more information on assessment instruments in occupational therapy, see Asher, I. E. (1996). *Occupational therapy assessment tools: An annotated index* (2nd ed.). Bethesda, MD: American Occupational Therapy Association.

References

Bergner, M., Bobbit, R. A., Carter, W. B., & Gilson, B. S. (1981). The Sickness Impact Profile: Development and final revision of a health status measure. *Medical Care, 19,* 787–805.

Braun, S., Msall, M. E., & Granger, C. V. (1991). *Manual for the Functional Independence Measure for Children.* Buffalo, NY: Center for Functional Assessment Research, Uniform Data System for Medical Rehabilitation, State University of New York.

Brown, M., Gordon, W. A., & Diller, L. (1984). Rehabilitation indicators. In A. S. Halpern & M. S. Fuhrer (Eds.), *Functional assessment in rehabilitation* (pp. 187–203). Baltimore: Paul H. Brooks.

Corrigan, J. D., & Deming, R. (1995). Psychometric characteristics of the community integration questionnaire: Replication and extension. *Journal of Head Trauma Rehabilitation, 10*(4), 41–53.

Data Management Service of the Uniform Data System for Medical Rehabilitation and the Center for Functional Assessment Research, State University of New York at Buffalo. (1993). *Guide for the Uniform Data Set for Medical Rehabilitation* (4th ed.). Buffalo, NY: Author.

Gowland, C., Stratford, P., Ward, M., Moreland, J., Torresin, W., Van Hullenaar, S., Sanford, J., Barreca, S., Vanspall, B., & Plews, N. (1993). Measuring physical impairment and disability with the Chedoke-McMaster Stroke Assessment. *Stroke, 24,* 58–63.

Haley, S., Coster, W., Ludlow, I., Jaltiwanger, J., & Andrellos, P. (1992). *Pediatric*

Evaluation of Disability Inventory (PEDI): Development, standardization, and administration manual. Boston: New England Medical Center.

Harvey, R. F., & Jellinek, H. M. (1981). Functional performance measurement: A program approach. *Archives of Physical Medicine and Rehabilitation, 62,* 456–460.

Harwood, R. H., Gompertz, P., & Ebrahims, S. (1994). Handicap 1 year after stroke: Validity of a new scale. *Journal of Neurology, Neurosurgery and Psychiatry, 57,* 825–829.

Hébert, R., Carrier, R., & Bilodeau, A. (1988). The Functional Autonomy Measurement System (SMAF): Description and validation of an instrument for the measurement of handicaps. *Age and Aging, 17,* 293–302.

Katz, S., Ford, A. B., Moskowitz, R. W., Jackson, B. A., & Jaffe, M. W. (1963). Studies of illness in the aged. The index of ADL: A standardized measure of biological and psychosocial function. *Journal of the American Medical Association, 185,* 914–919.

Klein, R. M., & Bell, B. (1982). Self-care skills: Behavioral measurement with the Klein-Bell ADL Scale. *Archives of Physical Medicine and Rehabilitation, 63,* 335–338.

Kohlman Thomson, L. (1992). *Kohlman Evaluation of Living Skills* (KELS) (3rd ed.). Rockville, MD: American Occupational Therapy Association.

Law, M., Baptiste, S., Carswell-Opzoomer, A., McColl, M. A., Polatajko, H., & Pollock, N. (1994). *Canadian Occupational Performance Measure,* (2nd ed.). Toronto, Ontario: Canadian Association of Occupational Therapists Publications.

Mahoney, F. I., & Barthel, D. W. (1965). Functional evaluation: The Barthel Index. *Maryland State Medical Journal, 14,* 61–65.

Meenan, R. F. (1982). Arthritis Impact Measurement Scales (AIMS) approach to health status measurement: Conceptual background and measurement properties. *Journal of Rheumatology, 9,* 785–788.

Nguyen, T. D., Attkisson, C. C., & Stegner, B. L. (1983). Assessment of patient satisfaction: Development and refinement of a service evaluation questionnaire. *Evaluation and Program Planning, 6,* 299–314.

Oliver, R., Blathwayt, J., Brackley, C., & Tamaki, T. (1993). Development of the Safety Assessment of Function and the Environment for Rehabilitation (SAFER). *Canadian Journal of Occupational Therapy, 60,* 78–82.

Pascoe, G. C., & Attkisson, C. C. (1983). The Evaluation Ranking Scale: A new methodology for assessing satisfaction. *Evaluation and Program Planning, 6,* 335–347.

Ware, J. E., & Hays, R. D. (1988). Methods for measuring patient satisfaction with specific medical encounters. *Medical Care, 26,* 393–402.

Ware, J. E., Kosinski, M., & Keller, S. D. (1996). A 12-item short-form health survey: Construction of scales and preliminary tests of reliability and validity. *Medical Care, 34,* 220–233.

Ware, J., & Sherbourne, C. (1992). The Medical Outcomes Study 36-Item Short-Form Health Survey (SF-36). *Medical Care, 30,* 473–481.

Whiteneck, G. G., Clarlifue, S. W., Gerhart, K. A., Overholser, J. D., & Richardson, G. N. (1992). Quantifying handicap: A new measure of long-term rehabilitation outcomes. *Archives of Physical Medicine and Rehabilitation, 73,* 519–525.

Appendix B

Bibliography of Methodological Articles

Balas, E. A., Kretschmer, R. A. C., Gnann, W., West, D. A., Boren, S. A., Centor, R. M., Nerlich, M., Gupta, M., West, T. D., & Soderstrom, N. S. (1998). Interpreting cost analyses of clinical interventions. *Journal of the American Medical Association, 279*, 54–57.

Brouwer, W. B., Koopmanschap, M. A., & Rutten, F. F. (1997). Productivity costs measurement through quality of life? A response to the recommendations of the Washington Panel. *Health Economics, 6*, 253–259.

Canadian Coordinating Office for Health Technology Assessment. (1997). *Guidelines for economic evaluation of pharmaceuticals: Canada* (2nd ed.). Ottawa, Ontario: Author.

Drummond, M. F., O'Brien, B. J., Stoddart, G. L., & Torrance, G. (1997). *Methods for the economic evaluation of health care programmes* (2nd ed.). Oxford, UK: Oxford University Press.

Elixhauser, A., Luce, B. R., Taylor, W. R., & Reblando, J. (1993). Health care CBA/CEA: An update on the growth and composition of the literature. *Medical Care, 31*(7 Supplement), JS1–JS11.

Finkler, S. A. (1982). The distinction between cost and charges. *Annals of Internal Medicine, 96*, 102–109.

Fuchs, V. R. (1980). What is CBA/CEA, and why are they doing this to us? *New England Journal of Medicine, 303*, 937–938.

Goeree, R. (Ed.). (1994). *Evaluation of programs for the treatment of schizophrenia: A health economic perspective*. Ottawa, Canada: Health Canada.

Gold, M. R., Siegel, J. E., Russell, L. B., & Weinstein, M. C. (1996). *Cost-effectiveness in health and medicine*. New York: Oxford University Press.

Johannesson, M. (1996). *Theory and methods of economic evaluation of health care*. Dordrecht, The Netherlands: Kluwer Academic Publishers.

Koopmanschap, M. A., & Rutten, F. F. (1996). A practical guide for calculating indirect costs of disease. *PharmacoEconomics, 10*, 460–466.

Krahn, M., & Gafni, A. (1993). Discounting in the economic evaluation of health care interventions. *Medical Care, 31*, 403–418.

Luce, B. R., Manning, W. G., Siegel, J. E., & Lipscomb, J. (1996). Estimating costs in cost-effectiveness analysis. In M. R. Gold, J. E. Siegel, L. B. Russell, & M. C. Weinstein (Eds.), *Cost-effectiveness in health and medicine.* (pp. 176–211). New York: Oxford University Press.

McCulloch, D. (1991). "Can we measure output?" Quality-adjusted life years, health indices and occupational therapy. *British Journal of Occupational Therapy, 54,* 219–221.

Menon, D., Schubert, F., & Torrance, G. W. (1996). Canada's new guidelines for the economic evaluation of pharmaceuticals. *Medical Care, 34*(12), DS77–DS86.

Rittenhouse, B. E. (1996). Is there a need for standardization of methods in economic evaluations of medicines? *Medical Care, 34*(12 Supplement), DS13–DS22.

Rittenhouse, B. E. (1997). Healthy years equivalents versus time trade-off: Ambiguity on certainty and uncertainty. *International Journal of Technology Assessment in Health Care, 13,* 1, 35–48.

Russell, L. B., Gold, M., Siegel, J. E., Daniels, N., & Weinstein, M. C. (1996). The role of cost-effectiveness analysis in health and medicine. *Journal of the American Medical Association, 276,* 1172–1177.

Shwartz, M., Young, D. W., & Siegrist, R. (1995). The ratio of costs to charges: How good a basis for estimating costs? *Inquiry, 32,* 476–481.

Siegel, J. E., Weinstein, M. C., Russell, L. B., & Gold, M. (1996). Recommendations for reporting cost-effectiveness analyses. *Journal of the American Medical Association, 276,* 133–1341.

Sloan, F. A. (1995). *Valuing health care: Costs, benefits, and effectiveness of pharmaceuticals and other medical technologies.* New York: Cambridge University Press.

Watson, D. E., & Mathews, M. (1998). Economic evaluation of occupational therapy: Where are we at? *Canadian Journal of Occupational Therapy, 65,* 160–167.

Weinstein, M. C., Siegel, J. E., Gold, M., Kamlet, M. S., & Russell, L.B. (1996). Recommendations of the Panel on Cost-Effectiveness in Health and Medicine. *Journal of the American Medical Association, 276,* 1253–1258.

Weinstein, M. C., & Stason, W. B. (1977). Foundations of cost-effectiveness analysis for health and medical practices. *New England Journal of Medicine, 296,* 716–721.

Wolff, N., Helminiak, T. W., & Tebes, J. K. (1997). Getting the cost right in cost-effectiveness analyses. *American Journal of Psychiatry, 154,* 736–743.

Zarnke, K. B., Levine, M. A. H., & O'Brien, B. J. (1997). Cost-benefit analyses in the health care literature: Don't judge a study by its label. *Journal of Clinical Epidemiology, 50,* 813–822.

Appendix C

Bibliography of Economic Evaluations

The articles listed in this Appendix provide examples of different types of economic evaluations that have been conducted in clinical areas that may be of interest to rehabilitation practitioners, administrators, and researchers.

Boyle, M. H., Torrance, G. W., Sinclair, J. C., & Horwood, S. P. (1983). Economic evaluation of neonatal intensive care of very-low-birth-weight infants. *New England Journal of Medicine, 308*, 1330–1337.

Edwards, M., Law, M., Worth, B., & Baptiste, S. (1995). Evaluation of the cost effectiveness of therapist computerized entry of occupational therapy workload measurement data. *Canadian Journal of Occupational Therapy, 62*, 95–99.

Feldman, P. H., Latimer, E., & Davidson, H. (1996). Medicaid-funded home care for the frail elderly and disabled: Evaluating the cost savings and outcomes of a service delivery reform. *Health Services Research, 31*, 489–509.

Fenton, F. R., Tessier, L., Contandriopoulos, A., Nguyen, H., & Struening, E. L. (1982). A comparative trial of home and hospital psychiatric treatment: Financial costs. *Canadian Journal of Psychiatry, 27*, 177–187.

Garber, A. M., & Fenerty, J. P. (1991). Costs and benefits of prenatal screening for cystic fibrosis. *Medical Care, 29*, 473–491.

Gladman, J., Whynes, D., & Lincoln, N. (1994). Cost comparison of domiciliary and hospital-based stroke rehabilitation. *Age and Aging, 23*, 24–245.

Gold, M., Gafni, A., Nelligan, P., & Millson, P. (1997). Needle exchange programs: An economic evaluation of a local experience. *Canadian Medical Association Journal, 157*, 255–262.

Hisashige, A. (1994). Health economic analysis of the neonatal screening program in Japan. *International Journal of Technology Assessment in Health Care, 10*, 382–391.

Holmquist, L. W., de Pedro Cuesta, J., Möller, G., Holm, M., & Sidén, Å. (1996). A pilot study of rehabilitation at home after stroke: A health-economic appraisal. *Scandinavian Journal of Rehabilitation Medicine, 28,* 9–18.

Johnston, M. V., & Miller, L. S. (1986). Cost-effectiveness of the Medicare three-hour regulation: Physical plus occupational therapy. *Archives of Physical Medicine and Rehabilitation, 67,* 581–585.

Keith, R. A., (1996). Rehabilitation after stroke: Cost-effectiveness analyses. *Journal of the Royal Society of Medicine, 89,* 631–633.

Kirz, H. L., & Larsen, C. (1986). Costs and benefits of medical student training to a Health Maintenance Organization. *Journal of the American Medical Association, 256,* 734–739.

Knapp, M., & Kavanagh, S. (1997). Economic outcomes and costs in the treatment of schizophrenia. *Clinical Therapeutics, 19,* 128–138.

Margolis, L. H., & Petti, R. D. (1994). An analysis of the costs and benefits of two strategies to decrease length in children's psychiatric hospitals. *Health Services Research, 29,* 155–167.

Meyers, S. K. (1995). Exploring the costs and benefit drivers of clinical education. *American Journal of Occupational Therapy, 49,* 107–111.

Oldridge, N., Furlong, W., Fenny, D., Torrance, G., Guyatt, G., Crowe, J., & Jones, N. (1993). Economic evaluation of cardiac rehabilitation soon after acute myocardial infarction. *American Journal of Cardiology, 72,* 154–161.

Rich, M. W., Bechham, V., Wittenberg, C., Leven, C., Freedland, K. E., & Carney, R. M. (1995). A multidisciplinary intervention to prevent the readmission of elderly patients with congestive heart failure. *New England Journal of Medicine, 333,* 1190–1195.

Rissanen, P., Aro, P., Sintonen, H., Asikainen, K., Slätis, P., & Paavolainen, P. (1997). Costs and cost-effectiveness in hip and knee replacements: A prospective study. *International Journal of Technology Assessment in Health Care, 13,* 575–588.

Rizzo, J. A., Baker, D. I., McAvay, G., & Tinetti, M. E. (1996). The cost-effectiveness of a multifactorial targeted prevention program for falls among community elderly persons. *Medical Care, 34,* 954–969.

Ruchlin, H. S., & Morris, J. N. (1981). Cost-benefit analysis of an emergency alarm and response system: A case study of a long-term care program. *Health Services Research, 16,* 65–80.

Shalik, L. D. (1987). Cost-benefit analysis of Level II fieldwork in occupational therapy. *American Journal of Occupational Therapy, 41,* 638–645.

Trahey, P. J. (1991). A comparison of the cost-effectiveness of two types of occupational therapy services. *American Journal of Occupational Therapy, 45,* 397–400.

Tucher, M. A., Davison, J. G., & Ogle, S. J. (1984). Day hospital rehabilitation—Effectiveness and cost in the elderly: A randomized controlled trial. *British Medical Journal, 289,* 1209–1212.

Appendix D

Answers to Practice Exercises

Chapter 2. Evaluating Clinical Services

1. Tinetti et al. (1994) determined that the intervention was associated with a 30% reduction in the rate of falls. These investigators conducted a clinical evaluation to assess the relationship between participation in an intervention program and a health outcome.

2. Rizzo, Baker, McAvay, and Tinetti (1996) conducted a cost-benefit analysis to assess the costs and financial benefits (i.e., economic outcomes) from participation in an intervention program.

3. Gold, Gafni, Nelligan, and Millson (1997) conducted a cost-effectiveness evaluation to assess the cost per case prevented and a cost-benefit analysis to determine the net financial effect of delivering the intervention.

4. Rissanen et al. (1997) conducted a cost-effectiveness analysis to compare the costs and effects of the surgery on changes in disability status. A cost-utility analysis was conducted when they compared the cost per change in quality of life among service recipients.

5. Oldridge et al. (1993) conducted a cost-utility analysis to assess the incremental costs of offering the program and the effect of this intervention on the quality and quantity of life of service recipients.

6. Clark et al. (1997) conducted a clinical evaluation to assess the relationship between participation in an intervention program and a health outcome.

Chapter 3. Designing and Managing an Evaluation

1. The service alternatives include the receipt of prevention services or routine care. The second alternative represents current practice that could include the delivery of medical and rehabilitation services for persons who fall and injure themselves, no services for those who fall but do not seek intervention, or for persons who do not fall.

2. The charges associated with the delivery of the fall prevention program (i.e., start-up and operational costs) represent the resource contributions or costs that should be included in the evaluation. The economic outcomes of interest include the fiscal effect of any alterations in the health service use patterns of the elderly persons who participate in the program.

3. A possible research question might be: "From a payer perspective, is a prevention program that is designed to reduce the frequency of falls among high-risk elderly who live in the community preferable to the current approach of fracture management in terms of annual net financial effect?"

Chapter 4. Cost-Consequence and Cost-Effectiveness Analyses

1. The perspective of the analysis should be the payer as this is the audience for whom the evaluation report is targeted. There are two payers in this scenario: (a) the employer pays premiums to the health plan; and (b) the health plan pays the service provider's charges.

2. Figure 9 illustrates how the conceptual framework provided in chapter 2 could be applied to this clinical example.

3. A cost-consequence analysis should provide a descriptive summary of a health service and may compare this intervention to another program or the delivery of no return-to-work intervention. This description states the costs and consequences (i.e., health and economic outcomes) of the alternative services.

4. Cost-effectiveness analyses require that the costs and outcomes of the primary service (e.g., return-to-work program) be compared with the costs and outcomes of the most appropriate alternative service (e.g., not participating in the return-to-work program). Therefore, the incremental costs and incremental outcomes are most relevant to report unless persons in the target audience seek information regarding the full cost of either service. The investigators would report the cost to payers for providing the return-to-work program to eligible employees. The relevant costs are the expenses the payers incur above and beyond (i.e., incremental costs) those that they would have incurred had the employee not participated in the program. The health outcomes included in the cost-effectiveness ratio would be those that the employees would attain above and beyond (i.e., incremental outcomes) those that they would have achieved had they not participated in the program. Ultimately, it would be appropriate to state the differences in cost per unit of outcome between the two service alternatives (i.e., participating versus not participating in the return-to-work program).

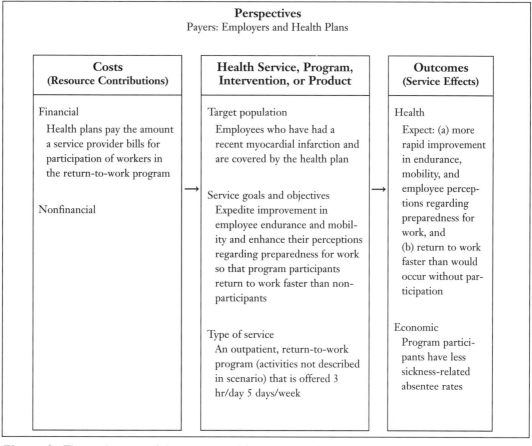

Figure 9. The application of the conceptual framework offered in chapter 2 to a clinical example.

5. Table 12 provides a summary as to how costs and outcomes vary by the perspective used to conduct the evaluation.

Chapter 5. Cost-Utility and Cost-Benefit Analyses

1. Level II fieldwork occurs within health service organizations after completion of the academic portion of students' curriculum. Students receive supervision from staff members within the organization, and the experience typically lasts for 13 weeks.

2. The evaluation will provide decision makers in health service organizations with information regarding the relative value of offering versus not offering fieldwork experiences. Therefore, the comparative service alternative is the scenario where fieldwork is not offered.

3. As the results of the evaluation will be used to recruit and retain fieldwork sites, the evaluation should be performed from the perspective of

Table 12
The Costs and Outcomes of a Clinical Service by Perspective

	Costs (Resource Contributions)		Outcomes (Service Effects)	
Perspective	Financial	Nonfinancial	Health	Economic
Health care provider	Labor (direct and indirect), material, equipment, and overhead costs		May alter job satisfaction of staff member	Participation in the return-to-work program may alter an employee's future use patterns
Patient/client	Health plan premiums Copays and deductibles Travel expenses	Extra time receiving outpatient care	Endurance, mobility, and perception of preparedness to return to work	A change in employment income would occur if one returned to work sooner (+ benefit) or later (– benefit) after participating in the program
Societal	Opportunity cost of labor (direct and indirect), material, equipment, and over-head costs Travel expenses	Extra time receiving outpatient care	Endurance, mobility, and perception of preparedness to return to work are enhanced and/or attained more quickly Incremental benefits in over-all health status and well-being	A change in employment income would occur if employees return to work sooner (+ benefit) or later (– benefit) after participating in the program Any alteration in family income due to changes in productivity of spouse or significant other

decision makers within fee-for-service health service organizations. Refer to Shalik (1987) for a discussion regarding the determination of costs and benefits from a fee-for-service organizational perspective and to Kirz and Larsen (1986) for a discussion regarding the determination of costs and benefits from a prepaid managed care organization point-of-view.

4. The costs that should be included in the analysis are the financial (i.e., start-up and operational costs) and nonfinancial resource contributions important and relevant to decision makers in health service organizations. Therefore, it is important to determine the organizational resources that would be used to offer fieldwork. The primary resource is personnel time as staff members will be required to orient, supervise, and evaluate students. Secondary costs include some office supplies and space. As these secondary costs are only marginal, the evaluation should focus on measuring and valuing staff member time. Refer to chapter 7 regarding the methods used to conduct cost analyses.

5. The amount of time that personnel allocate toward different activities is most easily measured in minutes, therefore this should be the unit of measurement. The value of staff member time is equivalent to the cost that a health service organization passes on to offer fieldwork. In a fee-for-service context, staff member costs are equal to the revenue that would be generated by the staff member if they had allocated this time to patient care rather than educational activities.

6. As described in Chapter 6, the most relevant and important outcomes that should be included in any analysis are health and economic. In the context of conducting a cost-benefit analysis of fieldwork from the perspective of health organizations, there are no health outcomes to measure and value, but there may be other intangible outcomes such as alterations in patient satisfaction, quality of care, service delivery education, and job satisfaction of clinical supervisors. Refer to Kirz and Larsen (1986) for an evaluation of these outcomes after implementation of a medical student training program at a health maintenance organization.

Arguably, students may not be as effective or may be more effective than occupational therapists at improving the health of the client. Ultimately, health service organizations must be responsible for the future cost of offering more services because of this difference in effectiveness. If health service organizations believe that this is true, then an assessment regarding the relative effectiveness of students and occupational therapists would be warranted, and investigators would then have to translate any significant differences in health outcomes between the two scenarios (i.e., service provided by occupational therapists vs. students) into financial outcomes.

The economic outcomes of offering fieldwork experiences to Level II students include the time students spend providing billable services to the client, doing administrative work, and providing any in-service training to staff members. Each of these outcomes represents an economic and financial benefit to health care organizations.

7. As with staff member resources, the amount of time that students allocate to different activities is most easily measured in minutes, therefore this should be the unit of measurement. The value of student time is dependent on the activity. Time spent providing billable services should be valued at the billing rate whereas time spent conducting administrative work or providing in-service training should be valued at the price providers pay other persons (i.e., staff members) to perform these activities.

8. As described in Chapter 3, this research question should provide a brief description of the service, outline the scope of the evaluation, define the perspective and time horizon of the assessment, and identify the relevant costs and outcomes included in the analysis. Therefore, the purpose of the evaluation is to assess the relative[16] financial costs and benefits (i.e., scope of evaluation) that accrue to a health care organization (i.e., service provider perspective) that provides an educational opportunity to students who have completed the academic phase of their education (i.e., service description). The evaluation will only include financial costs of teaching time and economic benefits in terms of additional charges (i.e., relevant costs and outcomes) over the course of a 13-week placement (i.e., time horizon).

Chapter 6. Identifying and Measuring the Outcomes of Clinical Services

1. A health care organization.

2. The primary service is the group therapy program (i.e., one session per week for 8 weeks) for adult women who have fibromyalgia, and the alternative service is the delivery of group therapy over the course of 5 weeks.

3. Box 2 indicates that service providers reportedly value functional and mobility status but provide educational activities. This stakeholder group represents the target audience of the evaluation report. However, consumers value disease-specific knowledge as well as functional status. These domains of health could be selected as potential outcome indica-

---

[16]Notice that the term *relative* is used in this context. The financial costs and benefits being considered are relative to those that would accrue if the service (i.e., fieldwork education) was not offered.

tors. In addition, if the intervention enhances disease-specific knowledge and functional status, participants in the program might make less use of health services (e.g., primary care physicians). This change in future health service use would represent a potential economic outcome.

4. The independent variable is the delivery of group therapy (i.e., 5- vs. 8-week intervals), whereas the dependent variable is basic activities of daily living (BADL).

5. These service alternatives can be compared on the basis of "cost per unit of change in BADL." As one service is provided over the course of 5 weeks whereas the other is offered for 8 weeks, the incremental cost and incremental benefit of the additional 3 weeks could be calculated using the cost-effectiveness ratio. Refer to chapter 4.

6. As the primary outcome is BADL of women with fibromyalgia, it is important to identify an instrument that has adequate content validity. As this tool might be used to assess change in service recipients over time, interrater and test–retest reliability as well as responsiveness are important psychometric properties.

Chapter 7. Identifying the Costs of Clinical Services

1. Refer to Table 13 for an example of a cost assessment using standard figures.

2. Use Table 14 to compute the financial cost to deliver this service.

3. As equipment costs represent historic costs, they are not relevant to decisions regarding the delivery of services in the future. This type of cost would only be relevant if new equipment was required. The proportion of the overhead that is associated with the amortization of prior capital expenditures is also irrelevant, but overhead costs associated with heating, etc. are appropriate. Therefore, the most relevant costs to decision makers regarding the delivery of these new services are the expenditures associated with labor, material, and overhead.

4. The incremental cost of offering Service A is approximately $1,300. This is calculated by determining the sum of the cost of Service A (i.e., labor = $1,255, material = $35, overhead = $1,216) less the cost of Service B (i.e., labor = $619, overhead = $595). The type of economic evaluation that was just conducted is a cost-minimization.

Chapter 8. Enhancing Methodological Rigor

1. a. The investigators used a stratified, random assignment, crossover research design with a "washout" period. In addition, this is a "single-blind" study. This research design helped the evaluators to select participants based on certain characteristics to enhance the

Table 13
Example of a Cost Assessment of a Clinical Service: Intensive Service

Step 1. Identify Resource Contributions	Step 2. Measure and Value the Resource Contributions Consumed			
	Quantity of Contributions Consumed To Deliver the Service (Q)	Price per Unit (P)	Cost of Contributions (Q × P)	Subtotal
1. Labor costs				
A. Clinical				
Evaluation	1 hr	$33.65[a]	33.65	
Direct intervention	25.8 hr[b]	33.65	868.17	
Cast fabrication	1.5 hr	33.65	50.47	
Indirect[c]	6.45 hr[d]	33.65	217.04	
B. Administrative support	2.15 hr[e]	40.00[f]	86.00	
			Estimated total cost of labor:	$1,255.33
2. Material costs				
Casting materials		35.00	35.00	
			Estimated total cost of material:	$35.00
3. Equipment costs				
Therapy equipment	25.8 hr	10.00[g]	258.00	
Casting equipment	1.5 hr	8.00[h]	12.00	
			Estimated total cost of equipment:	$270.00
4. Other				
Overhead	34.75 hr[i]	35.00[j]	1,216.25	
			Estimated total cost of overhead:	$1,216.25
			FULL COST	$2,800 per child[k]

(continued)

Table 13 (continued)

Note. As a large portion of the cost estimate in this table is based on assumptions regarding the cost of certain resources, a sensitivity analysis will be conducted on this assessment in the Practice Exercises in chapter 8.

[a]In 1997, the average annual full-time salary of an occupational therapist was $47,095 (*OT Week*, January 29, 1998, p. 6). Employers must also cover other employee expenses (e.g., health benefits), therefore it is assumed for this scenario that the average annual cost to employ an occupational therapist is $70,000. The amount of $70,000 divided by 52 weeks/year divided by 40 hr/week equals an hourly cost of $33.65.

[b]This intervention was provided for 45 min twice weekly for 4 months. There are 4.3 weeks/month on average as there are 52 weeks/year and 12 months (i.e., 52 ÷ 12 = 4.3). Therefore, 45 min multiplied by twice weekly intervention multiplied by 4.3 weeks/month multiplied by a 4-month treatment duration (i.e., 45 × 2 × 4.3 × 4) equals the total amount of intervention time (i.e. 1,548 min). This value divided by 60 min/hr equals the total amount of intervention time in hours (i.e., 25.8 hr).

[c]Indirect labor refers to time spent to prepare or document the assessment results and intervention.

[d]Planning (e.g., prepare home program) and documentation at a rate of 15 min/hr of direct treatment equals 6.45 hr.

[e]Clinical and administrative supervision charged at a rate of 5 min/hr of direct intervention.

[f]Estimated cost of administrative overhead cost.

[g]Hypothetically, the cost of equipment can be determined by using the monetary value of the annual depreciation associated with the cost of purchasing the equipment and information regarding annual use of the equipment. When a piece of therapy equipment is purchased, accountants amortize or depreciate the cost of this investment over the useful life of the product. For example, a $500 piece of equipment that is expected to last 10 years will be depreciated at a rate of $50/year. In actuality, most medical equipment is depreciated at a standard rate that is determined by the Internal Revenue Service. For the purpose of this scenario, assume that the value of the annual depreciation associated with the equipment used to provide the service is $5,000. This cost should be shared among persons who use the equipment over the course of the year in accordance with the degree to which they use it (i.e., those who use the equipment more are associated with higher costs to the provider). If it is estimated that this equipment is used for approximately 500 hr/year, the cost of using the equipment on an hourly basis is $10. Ten dollars per hour multiplied by 25.8 hr of use is equal to $258. Refer to Question 3 in this chapter for a discussion regarding sunk costs.

[h]Calculated using the same method as outlined in the section "Therapy Equipment."

[i]Calculated based on the total amount of clinical resource time devoted to the service. Administrative time is not included as it is assumed that this resource is used concurrently to clinical services.

[j]Based on figures derived from the accounting department regarding the cost per hours of operation and incorporating operating expenses (e.g., heating, wages of accountants and support personnel). This cost per hour of operation would be shared among all persons who use the facility within each hour.

[k]This value has been rounded to the nearest $100 to estimate of the full cost of the service, as reporting financial figures to the nearest dollar tends to suggest certainty regarding the accuracy of this value. This figure assumes that intervention was given on a one-to-one basis and that children were not seen for group therapy.

Table 14
Example of a Cost Assessment of a Clinical Service: Regular Service

Step 1. Identify Resource Contributions	Step 2. Measure and Value the Resource Contributions Consumed			
	Quantity of Contributions Consumed To Deliver the Service (Q)	Price per Unit (P)	Cost of Contributions (Q × P)	Subtotal
1. Labor costs				
A. Clinical				
Evaluation	1 hr	$33.65[a]	$33.65	
Direct intervention	12.9 hr[b]	33.65	434.08	
Indirect[c]	3.23 hr[d]	33.65	108.69	
B. Administrative support	1.08 hr[e]	40.00[f]	43.20	
		Estimated total cost of labor:		$619.62
2. Material costs				
		Estimated total cost of material:		$00
3. Equipment costs				
Therapy equipment	12.9 hr	10.00[g]	129.00	
		Estimated total cost of equipment:		$129.00
4. Other				
Overhead	17 hr[h]	35.00[i]	595.00	
		Estimated total cost of overhead:		$595.00
		FULL COST		$1,300 per child[j]

Note. As a large portion of the cost estimate in this table is based on assumptions regarding the cost of certain resources, a sensitivity analysis will be conducted on this assessment in the Practice Exercises in chapter 8.

[a]Refer to Appendix D Table 13.

[b]This intervention was provided for 45 min once weekly for 4 months. There are 4.3 weeks/month on average as there are 52 weeks/year and 12 months (i.e., $52 \div 12 = 4.3$). Therefore, 45 min multiplied by weekly intervention multiplied by 4.3 weeks/month multiplied by a 4-month treatment duration (i.e., $45 \times 1 \times 4.3 \times 4$) equals the total amount of intervention time (i.e. 774 min). This value divided by 60 min/hr equals the total amount of intervention time in hours (i.e., 12.9 hr).

(continued)

external validity of findings by way of stratified sampling and to control for case-mix differences between groups by way of random assignment of participants to the initial intervention group. The use of participants as their own control group was attained by way of the crossover design. This last feature was deemed to be necessary due to the large between-participant variability in outcomes seen in prior studies. The washout period limited carry-over effects, and the researchers were careful to blind evaluators (i.e., single-blind) who measured outcomes on an attempt to limit the effect of this potential source of bias.

b. Although all of the participants in this study were from eight rehabilitation centers, the authors did not declare how these facilities were recruited, and any selection bias that may have arisen from this process was not described.

2. A sensitivity analysis is provided in Table 15. The approximate cost of the intensive intervention ranges from $2,600 to $3,100, whereas the approximate cost of regular services ranges from $1,200 to $1,500.

Chapter 10. Demonstrating Results With Graphic Illustrations

See Figures 10 and 11. ❖

---

cIndirect labor refers to time spent to prepare or to document the assessment results and intervention.

dPlanning and documentation at a rate of 15 min/hr of direct treatment equals 3.23 hr.

eClinical and administrative supervision charged at a rate of 5 min/hr of direct intervention.

fEstimated cost of administrative overhead cost.

gRefer to Appendix D Table 13.

hRefer to Appendix D Table 13.

iRefer to Appendix D Table 13.

jThis value has been rounded to the nearest $100 to estimate the full cost of the service. Refer to Appendix D Table 13.

Table 15
Sensitivity Analysis of Cost Assessment
(Intensive Neurodevelopmental Treatment Versus Regular Occupational Therapy)

Resources	Intensive		
	Quantity (hours of use)	Price	Costs
1. Labor Costs			
A. Clinical			
Evaluation	1.00	$33.65	$33.65
Treatment	25.80	33.65	868.17
Cast fabrication	1.50	33.65	50.48
Indirect	6.45	33.65	217.04
B. Administrative	2.15	40.00	86.00
			Total labor $1,255.34
2. Material costs		35.00	
			Total material $35.00
3. Equipment Costs			
Therapy	25.80	10.00	258.00
Casting	1.50	8.00	12.00
			Total equipment $270.00
4. Overhead	34.75	35.00	1,216.25
			Total overhead $1,216.25
			$2,776.59

Resources	Intensive		
	Quantity (hours of use)	Price	Costs
1. Labor Costs			
A. Clinical			
Evaluation	1.00	$33.65	$33.65
Treatment	12.90	33.65	434.09
Indirect	3.23	33.65	108.68
B. Administrative	1.08	40.00	43.20
			Total labor $619.62
2. Material costs			
			Total material $0.00
3. Equipment Costs			
Therapy	12.90	10.00	129.00
			Total equipment $129.00
4. Overhead	17.13	35.00	599.55
		sub	Total overhead $599.55
			$1,348.17

Intensive (Overhead at $30 per hour)			Intensive (Overhead at $45 per hour)		
Quantity (hours of use)	Price	Costs	Quantity (hours of use)	Price	Costs
1.00	$33.65	$33.65	1.00	$33.65	$33.65
25.80	33.65	868.17	25.80	33.65	868.17
1.50	33.65	50.48	1.50	33.65	50.48
6.45	33.65	217.04	6.45	33.65	217.04
2.15	40.00	86.00	2.15	40.00	86.00
		Total labor $1,255.34			Total labor $1,255.34
	35.00			35.00	
		Total material $35.00			Total material $35.00
25.80	10.00	258.00	25.80	10.00	258.00
1.50	8.00	12.00	1.50	8.00	12.00
		Total equipment $270.00			Total equipment $270.00
34.75	30.00	1,042.50	34.75	45.00	1,563.75
		Total overhead $1,042.50			Total overhead $1,563.75
		$2,602.84			$3,124.09

Regular OT (Overhead at $30/hour)			Regular OT (Overhead at $45/hour)		
Quantity (hours of use)	Price	Costs	Quantity (hours of use)	Price	Costs
1.00	$33.65	$33.65	1.00	$33.65	$33.65
12.90	33.65	434.09	12.90	33.65	434.09
3.23	33.65	108.68	3.23	33.65	108.68
1.08	40.00	43.20	1.08	40.00	43.20
		Total labor $619.62			Total labor $619.62
		Total material $0.00			Total material $0.00
12.90	10.00	129.00	12.90	10.00	129.00
		Total equipment $129.00			Total equipment $129.00
17.13	30.00	513.90	17.13	45.00	770.85
		Total overhead $513.90			Total overhead $770.85
		$1,262.52			$1,519.47

Note. OT = occupational therapy.

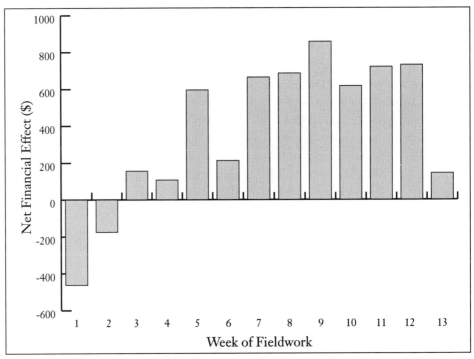

Figure 10. Net financial effect of offering Level II fieldwork by week (*n* = 156).

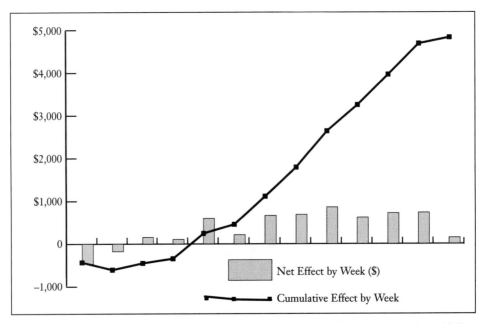

Figure 11. Net financial effect of Level II fieldwork: Weekly and cumulative (*n* = 156).

Index